I Am Somebody

Bringing Dignity and Compassion to Alzheimer's Caregiving

I Am Somebody

BRINGING DIGNITY AND COMPASSION TO ALZHEIMER'S CAREGIVING

Frances H. Kakugawa

WATERMARK
PUBLISHING

ISBN: 978-1-935690-59-7 (print edition)
ISBN: 978-1-935690-60-3 (e-book edition)

Library of Congress Control Number: 2014953810

Design and production by Dawn Sakamoto Paiva

Cover photo: iStock.com/FredFroese
Author's photo: Jason Y. Kimura

Watermark Publishing
1000 Bishop Street, Suite 806
Honolulu, Hawai'i 96813
Telephone (toll-free): 1-866-900-BOOK
Website: www.bookshawaii.net

Printed in the United States of America

*Dedicated to all caregivers
to preserve for future generations
the lessons of what it means to be human*

Other Books by Frances H. Kakugawa

For Caregivers

Mosaic Moon: Caregiving Through Poetry
Breaking the Silence: A Caregiver's Voice

Children's Books

Wordsworth the Poet
Wordsworth Dances the Waltz
Wordsworth! Stop the Bulldozer!

Memoirs

Teacher, You Look Like a Horse!
Lessons from the Classroom
Kapoho: Memoir of a Modern Pompeii

Poetry

The Path of Butterflies
Golden Spike
White Ginger Blossom
Sand Grains

The award-winning author of eleven books, and a regular column, "Dear Frances," for caregivers, Frances H. Kakugawa conducts workshops and lectures throughout the country. In her sessions for adults, Frances shares with honesty and openness the lessons learned from caregiving. Programs for hospital and elder-healthcare professionals focus on humanizing caregiving skills. In her children's workshops, Frances introduces students to writing as a way to explore and embrace the aging process and other aspects of their lives.

To book Frances for a workshop, classroom visit or lecture, email her at fhk@francesk.org or contact her online on her Facebook Page (www.facebook.com/FrancesKakugawa) or on her blog (franceskakugawa.wordpress.com).

Table of Contents

A Poet's Declaration

I am a star
In the Milky Way.
I am the crest
On emerald waves.
I am a dewdrop, crystal clear,
Capturing sunbeams in the morning mist.
I am that dust
On butterfly wings.
I am that song
Of a thousand strings.
I am that teardrop
You have kissed.
I am a poet!
I am! I am!
I am that rage
In the thunderstorm.
I am that image
Of a thousand form.
I am magic on each page.
I am a poet!
I am! I am!

Caregivers

SOS!

I'm shipwrecked

On this Isle of Caregivers

Send Help!

A bottle, sealed with wax

Washes up to shore. Inside,

A pen and sheets of blank paper.

When I first began caring for my mother, I used her voice in a poem I called "Emily Dickinson, I'm Somebody" (page 42). Later, a line from the poem, "I would if I could," spoken in my mother's voice, came to haunt me and became my mantra whenever I wanted to shout in exasperation, "Why did you?" or "Why didn't you?"

My own writing reminded me that her behavior was a result of this disease, beyond her control and mine. I came to believe that above all else, if I honored the human dignity in both of us, my mother and myself, then I would become a compassionate, loving and capable caregiver—because in the end, whatever we do to others, we do to ourselves.

In 2001, motivated to help other caregivers, I walked into the office of the president and CEO of the Alzheimer's Association—Aloha Chapter in Honolulu, Hawai'i with no appointment and volunteered to conduct a poetry workshop for people caring for loved ones afflicted with dementia.

And so we caregivers gathered, picked up our pens and wrote, wrote, wrote. The more we wrote, the faster the transformation. We were no longer just sons and daughters, wives and husbands, caught up in the relentless demands of day and night; now we were poet-caregivers, and that made all the difference in the world.

Words are hardly sufficient to describe the essence of what truly happened on our journey. Writing took us to a deeper level, beyond the physical aspects of caring, down to that depth where our own humanity resides. It was here we came to know what caregiving was going to be about. This gift of humanity, we like to call it, became a personal and private gift for each of us.

If you are a caregiver, you know of this unique world of caregiving, a world that becomes one of isolation and aloneness for both you and your loved one. A world that is filled with every possible emotion, along with the constant desire to do what is right.

To benefit from the lessons offered in this book, you don't need to be a writer or even harbor any aspirations to become one. For many caregivers, it is enough to know that their experience is shared by others, that there is someone out there who knows and understands the daily demands of what it means to be a caregiver. Those of us who have shared our writing in these pages understand the reality of being with someone who is gradually losing his or her own personhood—and we know what it is like to lose our own identity, too. For in caregiving, there are two of us: the caregiver and the one receiving care, both becoming defined by our roles.

To family and friends who are not primary caregivers, medical and health professionals, nursing home and adult care staff members—that is, to anyone who interacts with our loved ones—may this book give you glimpses into caregiving and help you become a more compassionate, understanding inhabitant of this world of caregivers and loved ones.

At my talks and presentations around the country, I am often asked, "Where can I find the poems that you read today?" You will find them here. Some are taken from my three previously published books on caregiving—*Mosaic Moon: Caregiving Through Poetry* (Watermark Publishing, 2002), *Wordsworth Dances the Waltz* (Watermark Publishing, 2007) and *Breaking the Silence: A Caregiver's Voice* (Willow Valley Press, 2010). Others represent new work from me and from caregivers I have come to know over the years.

When I started that first poetry workshop group in Honolulu, twelve caregivers joined me—ten women and two men. Five of those women chose to share their work, along with my own, in *Mosaic Moon*. *Breaking the Silence* featured the work of five different caregivers, along with a few contributions from a gentleman who attended one of my workshops claiming, "I don't write." In this new book, I am proud to introduce the work of eleven caregivers, some from the previous books, some new voices, who have joined me in exploring the caregiving experience. They are people who care for mothers, fathers, wives and husbands—men and women with a diverse range of cultural backgrounds, ages, faiths and education. In some of our shared writings, we speak for ourselves, expressing things we would never say aloud. In others, we speak with the voice of our loved ones, what we imagine they would say, if they could.

It is our hope that you will embrace these writings, find comfort and encouragement in them, and perhaps even pick up a pen and join us as poet-caregivers. But whether you choose to begin your own writing journey or not, we urge you to remember that both loved ones and caregivers deserve compassion, respect and a life with dignity. Each one of us is somebody. ✻

Frances H. Kakugawa

Mother Into Child, Child Into Mother

The same umbilical cord
That had once set me free
Now pulls and tugs me back
To where I had begun.

There must be hidden
Somewhere,
A gift very divine
In this journey back.

Some caregivers were introduced to caregiving without warning, an unannounced phone call that upends their lives. My own call came when I was deeply involved in my writing and work as an author and concentrating on my personal life,

having recently retired. The last thing I wanted to deal with was responsibility for someone else's life. It was a drastic change for me, just as it was for Elaine Okazaki, who wrote about her own fateful phone call in "Change" (page 18).

For other caregivers, the job crept in slowly, that thief known as Alzheimer's. It's only natural that the first signs of dementia are brushed off as signs of normal aging. This keeps us in the safe zone of denial until something drastic turns on an alarm. What are some of these early signs? Repeated questions, loss of memory, poor housekeeping, unpaid bills and changes in the household are a few examples. Once these are detected, it may be time for medical and family attention as safety and health are at stake. Bob Oyafuso had this type of gradual "call" to caregiving, as he chronicles in his poem, "Alzheimer's" (page 20).

Once the first step into the caregiving world has been taken — it doesn't matter how the journey began — caregivers devote their lives to their loved ones. This can reduce the caregiver to feeling like a non-person as both caregivers and their loved ones begin to merge into a single organisim. "Erasable Pencil #2" (page 25) and Jody Mishan's "Cave Life" (page 26) are about these feelings of being rubbed out and reduced to less than a full person. If we feel like this, how must our loved ones feel? This is why I feel bringing dignity into caregiving elevates both sides — when we treat our loved ones with dignity and honor, it is reflected back upon us.

The poems in this chapter take you into the world of caregiving. They offer a glimpse of what to expect and how others have come to fit in to this world. ✢

Caregiver Bio

· E L A I N E   O K A Z A K I ·

Ethel Natsuyo (1911–2006), a strong and determined woman, insisted that there was nothing wrong with her—it was her daughter, Elaine Okazaki, a retired teacher, who needed observation! Who would have thought that Ethel, a graduate of Mid-Pacific Institute and an accomplished seamstress at Shaheen's of Honolulu, would succumb to this dreaded illness. As Alzheimer's disease slowly crept through Ethel's "broken" mind and robbed her of capacity to think and perform independently, it became increasingly difficult for Elaine to maintain stability in both their lives. Elaine herself began experiencing physical ailments such as twitching eyelids, shortness of breath and facial distortions. Ethel was no longer the mother of Elaine's childhood and adult years, but Elaine still looks upon the time as a period during which both women provided care for each other. Elaine chuckles over memories of imaginary pictures that came alive, stashes of soiled clothing hidden throughout the bedroom and her mother's complaints of strangers sleeping with her. Today, Elaine resides in Honolulu, Hawai'i, and continues her role as volunteer docent with the Japanese Cultural Center of Hawai'i.

Where did it come from?
It began with one phone call
At 9:45 p.m., June 27, 2001
From Mom who identified herself

Change

ELAINE OKAZAKI

As Natsuyo, instead of Mom.
She had fallen, taken two hours
To crawl from the foot of her bed
To the nightstand for the telephone.

A rush to her home,
I find her in her bedroom,
Lights on.
A call to 911,
ER until the wee hours of the morn.
Finally to a vacant lot
Where I back my car into a pole.
Where did it come from?
This pole in a vacant lot?

Yes, where did it come from?

My lifestyle of art lessons,
Movies, restaurants,
Docent at the Japanese Cultural Center…
Immediately changed
With one phone call
From Mom who called herself
Natsuyo. ⁂

·BOB OYAFUSO·

Bob Oyafuso is a retired electrical engineer and caregiver for his wife, Fran, who is in her third year with Alzheimer's. Bob received his BS and MS degrees in electrical engineering from San Jose State University and spent his entire professional career in the highly competitive Bay Area. Fran (born in 1929) grew up in Southern California and after the end of her first marriage, moved to the Bay Area where she worked in her sister's medical office. Bob and Fran were married in 1981, making Bob an instant stepfather to five children. Fran is an accomplished artist and had a passion for dream interpretation, facilitating dream interpretation workshops and study groups for more than ten years. Together the couple was very involved in church activities at the Unitarian Universalists Society of Sacramento. Another great love was traveling, especially to Italy where they feasted on the art, food and beauty of the country. Bob has accepted his role as a caregiver and likes to use his skills as an engineer to make caregiving easier.

In the beginning it had no name
canceled vacations, skipped family
gatherings, failure to take medication
emails not answered, items misplaced.

Alzheimer's

BOB OYAFUSO

Then came the anger and accusations.
You're hiding things from me.
Why don't you listen to me.
Where have you been

I now know she has Alzheimer's
Deadly and beyond hope.
She knows not my name
nor her children's.

Her conversations are sprinkled
with what's his name, that person,
generous offer of money and a
willingness to help anyone.

There are children and animals
In an empty house
And the threat of violence
Is everywhere

The bathroom is any door
And any container is for trash
her toothbrush will clean face

and unravel her hair
She will wash the dishes
And I will do it again
Each day I see a little
Less of my wife

I see her struggle every day
With words, with walking
Alzheimer's has ravaged her brain
One neuron at a time ❧

Caregiver Bio

·RED SLIDER·

Red Slider is a poet, short story writer and essayist as well as woodworker, gardener and community activist. He lives in Northern California and was a caregiver for his mother, Isobel, for more than a decade, until her death in 2005. In her better days, Isobel served as a Peace Corps volunteer, was an educator, a reading specialist and diagnostician. She ran a reading clinic and maintained her practice until 1992. The works that appear in this anthology are taken from Red's chapbook, *Stewards of Mortality*, chronicling his experiences of caring for Isobel. Samples of other works can be found at www.holopoet.com and www. peacemonument.org.

It was an appointment at a clinic that began my journey with Isobel into the dark side of life's fragilities. It was on that day that I first understood the puzzling scruff marks on the top of her shoe as we climbed the clinic steps and her dragging toe scraped over each tread.

Little did I know then what terrible burdens were hidden in

Appointment Day

RED SLIDER

such a simple task as keeping an appointment. For the next fifteen years I would sadly come to learn the horror of the word, "appointment." But on that particular day (the first occasion on which I had ever accompanied Isobel on a visit to her doctor), it was just another appointment to see what was taking so long about diagnosing and treating some vague problem with her right foot and leg.

After that, there were inexorable waits as I followed along from diagnosis to diagnosis. What started as "drop foot" progressed to "shin splint" and then to "pinched nerve" and onward and upward as "carpal tunnel syndrome" until I finally could no longer sit idle and watch her "managed care" degenerate into "mangled care."

That was the beginning of our strange journey down this rabbit-hole of medical appointments. Alzheimer's wasn't even a word in our vocabulary at that time. It would be another year before we'd turn to that page in the dictionary. But the word "appointment" was, and its meaning loomed ahead of us in ways we could never have imagined. It was on that day of our first unsteady climb up the clinic stairs that I mark as the day, unbeknownst to either of us, I signed on as Isobel's caregiver. How could I have known then that I'd made an appointment that could not be canceled? ༄

There was no announcement
hardly a sound, a foot-scruff
on the steps to the clinic,
a slow walk, more delay
and no surprises.

Without
Appointment

RED SLIDER

Neither broadside nor listings
give date or time, fashionably late
for the spoon to drop
to the floor with a loud
Clang like a tin gong.

A door flung open
to a morning of strange sentences
mushed into vacant syllables
Da-da abbing, abba dobbing
over their own cadence.

Nothing is circled
on this calendar;
not the day her knees buckled,
the wild sounds in moan
or bone beat on thunder drum.

No one was on hand to introduce
the slump thing in the wheelchair,
with an RSVP that was never sent.
Forgive us for barging in this way.

Forgive us for being late, as usual.
Forgive us our sudden intrusion,
our insubordination, our guileless moon.
There, where there is matted grass,
our bewildered bare feet went. ❧

Erasable Pencil #2

FRANCES KAKUGAWA with RED SLIDER

How's your mother?
Is she sleeping through the night?
Is she taking her Aricept daily?
Is her Health Directive in order?
Her Living Trust? Who has
Power of Attorney?
How's her appetite?
Have you thought of Adult Day Care?
Have you looked for possible nursing home care?
Has her bed sore healed? Are you turning her over nightly?
Hello, this is the social worker. I still need to have the forms back.
This is all confidential, of course.
Hello, this is Medicare. Please call back. This concerns a wheelchair.
Hello, this is Medicare. Medicare doesn't cover your last visit.
Hello, this is your insurance company. Please call back.
Are you still taking her on walks?
You're such a good caregiver. Your mother is so lucky.
Will you donate to Alzheimer's Research?
Did you make your next appointment for your mother?

Her blood pressure's good. Everything looks good.
Stop! Stop! Stop!
You don't see me, do you?
You are vaporizing me
Right before your eyes.
When did you become
This giant eraser?

By the way, my name is Frances with an "e." ✄

Cave Life

JODY MISHAN

Don't come near me.
I'm infected with Caregiver
Depressionitis,
A particular kind of cootie
That will attack you with negativity,
Pick at you with criticism,
Disrespect your motives,
Ignore your attempts to help.

To avoid these inevitable misunderstandings
And embarrassing social disabilities,
I seek the darkness and anonymity of cave life.
Just going out to seek prey
And drag it home to me and my demented father. ✄

Caregiver Bio

· J O D Y   M I S H A N ·

Jody Mishan was an audio-visual writer/producer, travel magazine editor, and voice talent in Hawai'i for more than twenty years until her life and career were sidetracked, transformed and reinvented when her father, John, a retired Navy captain, was diagnosed with Alzheimer's disease. She became his primary caregiver for eight years until he passed in late 2006. Jody was one of the original poetry and journaling workshop members who participated in Frances' sessions at the Alzheimer's Association—Aloha Chapter. During her caregiving years, Jody was the public awareness coordinator for Kōkua Mau, Hawai'i's Hospice & Palliative Care Organization, working for the state hospices as part of a Robert Wood Johnson grant for the Hawai'i Executive Office on Aging (EOA) to improve care at the end of life. Since 2012, she has been the EOA coordinator for Hawai'i's first State Plan on Alzheimer's Disease and Related Dementias (www.hawaiiadrc.org/site/439/resources.aspx), working with the Task Force and now in the implementation process.

When did it go?

It visits so rarely, or not at all.

Will it ever return?

Buried under layers and layers of flab:

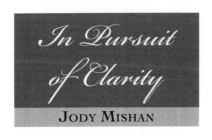

A fatty mental substance

Invading the brains of Alzheimer's caregivers.

No matter how hard you try

To keep up the appearance of normalcy and control

Of remembering details as before

Of getting something totally right, perfect...

Something always happens to show you ungracefully

That you can't think straight anymore.

You leave the house with only half of what you need.

Did you leave your brain in the refrigerator?

You forget to wear your watch.

You didn't bring the directions, the cell phone, the mail.

Forget to put on your ring you usually wear daily.

You put the milk in the freezer.

Is it that you can't wait to get away

And rush to escape the caregiver and your significantly "Other?"

Desperately seeking precious free time?

Or is it that you're trying too hard

To gather all the pieces of your own fragmented life?

And you have only several hours to do it.

A relay race
Before the next watch,
The next dinner planned,
The next long vigil,
The next chunk of hours,
Catering to you-know-who.
Monotonous routine supervision and coaching
Of your Alzheimer's-stricken loved one.
Your husband or wife, mother or father.

Details about them usurp your thinking process.
Doctors, appointments, groceries, toileting, policing,
Are they warm or cool enough,
Whoops, didn't lock the door, give them their pill.
They have grown like seeds of a banyan,
Like a smothering vine, carpeting your healthy branches.
Looking nice to the outside passersby.
But inside, oxygen-deprived.

Details usurp your clarity
Like a covert operation you're not aware of
Until it's too late.
You can't even detect now when it started.
Quickly and prolifically
The flab accumulates,
Obliterating your ability to reason.
Another day of less than perfect.
You can't find it when you need it anymore.

You make heroic efforts to take baby steps of
Managed and strategized daily work plans.

No matter how hard you try
Things that used to be easy and effortless
Take all your time and concentration.
You can't solve the simplest problems.
Another dose of stress knocks down your
Fragile house of toothpicks.

You can't plan.
You don't finish things.
Your head is full of noise
That no one else hears.
You're too vigilant to meditate.
Will you ever be able to think straight again?
You have faith you will.
But for now, you give up trying.
It feels too much like being retarded.
It's too scary to think it's contagious.
That you've become stupid. ✢

Are we caregivers all nerds?
Totally absorbed in one thing,
Isolated from the world,
No social life.

Nerds Anonymous

JODY MISHAN

Wearing uncool, ummatched clothing,
Repressed, self-conscious,
Able to relax only in the company
Of other caregivers.
Part of a system
That doesn't understand, help or support us.
Geeks. Nerds. Caregivers.
No dates on Satuday nights.
Not really party people.
Our humor is not normal anymore.
Hello. My name is Jody.
I'm a caregiver and I'm a nerd,
And I no longer have control of my life. ༈

Caregiver Bio

·L I N D A   N A G A T A·

Linda McCall Nagata was a long-distance care organizer for her mother Geraldine McCall (1916–1991). Gerry, as she preferred to be called, had been an elementary school secretary for many years. She enjoyed physical activities, such as skiing, and was a swimmer until the end of her life. She also loved to watch tennis and other sports on television. Though she showed signs of Alzheimer's in her early 60s, it was not until near the end of her life that a preliminary diagnosis was made. Linda made several trips to hire and organize help and to assist her father in dealing with the changing needs of her mother though it was difficult to manage the needs of her parents while raising two teens and working. Cancer took Gerry before she slipped into later stages of Alzheimer's. During the last few months of her life it was necessary to bring a case manager and companion into the picture to ensure that she had the help and oversight she needed. "Long-distance caregiving is a scary, worrisome task," Linda observes, "But I am ever so grateful that I had the opportunity to ensure my mother had the care she deserved and needed. It was wonderful to have those final months to talk to her in her lucid periods and tell her how much I loved her and what a great mom she had been."

I'm in the middle
Caught between an increasingly forgetful mother
And a rebellious daughter.

The Sandwich

LINDA NAGATA

Mom can't remember short-term things
She says inappropriate things
Acts in inappropriate ways
Dresses inappropriately
Happy one instant, crying the next.

Daughter is demanding and self-centered
Starts down the path of alcohol and drugs
Temper tantrums worth of a two-year-old
I am torn between two needy factions.
Mom unaware, daughter pushing all boundaries
Both out of control.

My strength seeps out.
The sound of my daughter's demanding voice,
Mom, crying and not understanding what is happening,
I am being pushed to the edge.
Is there anyone to help me? ◡

There will come a day;
and on that day
beings from beyond the stars
will come to ask,

The Caregiver's Reply

RED SLIDER

"Why should the likes of you,
defective and dangerous as you
are,
be permitted to spread beyond
the light of your dying sun
and onto the wonder of the heavens?"

In reply, a single caregiver
stepped out from the cloud of humanity
as if to say, "We are the Stewards of Mortality.
In all the limitless expanse of your travel,
the countless species of your wondrous universe,
have you ever met the likes of us?" ✺

The Alchemy of Caregivers

JODY MISHAN

Caregivers, unite in spirit!
What are you doing tonight?
What feelings have swept
you away,
Or rendered you numb,
Or made your heart sing?

Do you know how beautiful you are,

In your remote isolation?
I wish I could reward you
With each act of your gentle compassion.
Each unwitnessed touch of comfort.
I wish angels would lavish you with gifts
Every time you clean up a mess,
Or patiently tend your loved one
What if a bell would ring,
Or a team of award-givers would arrive at your doorstep,
With balloons and a million dollars,
When you've wiped a bottom for the thousandth time —
Caregivers' Clearinghouse.
Your heart and mine are one.
Made of the same spiritual essence.
We radiate the same colors.
Disconnected twins that search for each other
For completion.
I wish I could bring you your happiness again.
I wish peace would fill your soul,
So that you could catch a glimpse
Of the Heaven that awaits you.
In the meantime, God's Hands hold you.
Don't you know we're not alone?
So, stay strong, dear ones.
Keep lighting the darkness,
Spinning straw into gold.
Your harvest will come. ✸

If you could peek inside the caregiver,

Peel off the layer upon layer

Of exhaustion, scattered thoughts,

Any combination of ambivalent emotions,

Grotto

JODY MISHAN

You would be drawn into

A museum of artifacts.

You would want to linger more,

Drawn to artworks so subtle

And universal in relevance

That you would want to study them.

The caregiver's soul is an art form.

A marriage of craft and talent,

The result of which

Is tenderness, compassion, honor,

Vigilance, strength, courage.

An ocean of commitment.

A true heart.

A romantic spirit.

It is the profoundest beauty

That makes art.

That is the rock in the mine.

For so long not noticed,

Your attention casts a light

That would reveal

Glistening crystal clusters

Grown in the dark.

Now bathed in light, casting rainbows

In all directions. ﻌ

The Path Taken

What other path is there
Except the divine
Where love, kindness, compassion,
Help me discover little pieces of myself
That make me smile,
Bringing me such quiet joy
At the end of each day.
When she is gone,
The gift she gave me of myself
Will bring me such sadness
But lasting peace.

The challenges of caregiving—the physical burdens, the financial costs, the emotional turmoil, family strife and the disease itself, along with countless other unforeseen problems—often cause us to reduce our loved one to a "he" or a "she," a person devoid of all humanity.

I Am Somebody

·CHAPTER TWO·

Once I embraced the new person who was evolving before me, once I let go the person I wanted my mother to be, put myself in her position and educated myself on the disease and its effects on a person, caregiving turned into a freer flowing river. How gratifying to be able to pause now and then to say, "I am a good person after all." This was often accompanied by an inexplainable feeling of joy—joy in knowing I was able to rise above the burden of care.

A caregiver once attended my session saying, "I want to feel that joy you speak of." It wasn't long before she did. She learned to preserve her mother's dignity—and her own—by not seeing her as a patient whose voice was silenced by those around her, but as an individual with an identity, feelings and desires.

Setsuko "Sets" Yoshida, whose poems about her experience as a caregiver for her husband, Patrick, appear in this book, found herself on the opposite side of caregiving, being tended to by her son and his companion. She told me, as we sat for dinner one night, "The most difficult part of being cared for is the shame and the burden I have become to my son. The shame of knowing you need help in taking a bath or using the bathroom. It shames me so much to have my son see me like this. I think of how Patrick must have felt when I had to assist him with his personal functions."

Sets still has her voice, to let her wishes be known. But what of our loved ones with Alzheimer's who can no longer tell us their thoughts? If they could speak, what would they say? If we could hear their voices, wouldn't they help us become the most compassionate caregivers? If we paid attention to their voices, asking for compassion and dignity and human kindness, perhaps we would do our best to live up to these requests and enjoy a deeper dimension to our commitment to our life as caregivers.

It is easy to become consumed by caregiving and to allow it to take over our identity. Our lives revolve around doctor's appointments, dressing, feeding and cleaning up after our loved ones, ensuring that their affairs are in order. Their life becomes our life, our life becomes their life. Often help for the caregiver comes only as respite: a few days off, a brief walk, times when others share the caregiving load. Yet, after these momentary breaks, caregivers still return to an unchanged environment and to the same role.

How do we change that caregiving environment to help lessen the caregiver's load? Caregiving is not a role that can be shut off and on, becauses it is more than a physical role. It is deeply embedded in our psychological and emotional selves. For me, the moment I began to dignify and recognize the new person evolving before me, the moment I learned that whatever else was going on, if I honored dignity and compassion in my care, I could become the most compassionate and humanistic carer — and that made all the difference. By listening to the voices of our loved ones, the true help that we need to become a better caregiver will begin to take effect from the inside out — and this may be a more lasting relief from the daily demands.

To non-caregivers, continue to support caregivers as they search for this inner peace. Inquire about their well being, help them find time to enjoy their hobbies or to socialize with friends and remember, talk does not have to be limited to subjects related only to the world of caregiving. One of the best stories I heard was from caregiver Red Slider who often found his lawn mowed. To this day, the good Samaritans who performed this act of kindness remain anonymous. There is a need for more of this type of thoughtfulness among us. ༀ

If I could speak, this is what
My voice would say:

Do not let this thief scare you away.

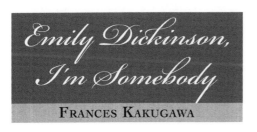

Emily Dickinson, I'm Somebody

FRANCES KAKUGAWA

Do not let this thief intimidate you
Into thinking I am no longer here.

When you see me, tell me quickly
Who you are.
Do not ask me, "Do you know me?"

Help me retain my own dignity
By not forcing me to say,
"No, I don't know who you are."
Save my face by greeting me
With your name even if the thief
Has stolen all that from me.
It shames me to such indignities
To know I do not know you.
Help me in this game of pretension
That this thief has not stolen
Your name from me.

My words have all forsaken me,
My thoughts are all gone.
But do not let this thief
Forsake you from me.
Speak to me for I am still here.
I understand hugs and smiles

And loving kindness.
Speak to me and not around me.
I am not a she or her or even a room number.

I am still here.
When I soil my clothing, or do something absurd
Do not tell me, "Why didn't you?"
If I could, I would.
I know I have turned
Into a monstrous baby,
If I could, I would not allow this thief
To let you live and see
What he has stolen from me.

I know my repeated questions
Are like a record player gone bad,
But my words are gone
And this is the only way I know
To make contact with you.
It is my sole way of saying,
Yes, I know you are here.
This thief has stolen
Everything else,
Except for these questions
And soon they, too, will be stolen away.

Yes, I am still here.
Help me retain my dignity.

Help me remain a human being
In this shell of a woman I have become.
I beg that you not violate the person I still am
In my world of silence.
I am still here.
Oh, I am still here. ❧

Office Visit with Dr. Tanabe

FRANCES KAKUGAWA

For Dr. Marianne Tanabe

*I'm certain, if I were a mind reader,
these would have been my mother's
thoughts each time she had an
appointment with her physician.*

Who is she, this woman
Who speaks so gently to me?
Is she my daughter? She must be.
Only a daughter would speak
with such care
And such kindness.
She doesn't call me Mother.
She must be someone
Whose face I cannot name.
Did someone call her Doctor?
She asked my permission
To put her stethoscope to my heart.
She thanked me for allowing her
to examine me.

Her fingers on my buttons are gentler than mine.
Her hands touch me oh so carefully.
She treats me like I'm crystal and fine china.
So much respect from someone
Whose face I do not know.

Who can she be this most gentle of people
Her voice is so filled with such joy and laughter;
She must be happy to be with me.
But who is she?
I am so confused, is she a daughter
Whose name I've lost?
But she doesn't call me mother.
I can't recall her name or her face.
But this much I know,
This is such a safe place to be.
With someone so gentle and kind.
Who is she? ✤

Hey Alzheimer's

FRANCES KAKUGAWA with RED SLIDER

Here is my mother's voice again through my pen.

Hey Alzheimer's,
Sitting there so smug, gloating
Over the memories
You have stolen, the years we
have lost.
Do I have a story to tell you.

You see, Alzheimer's,
What you think you took, we kept.
Every memory we secreted away
In our children, our friends,
Our loved ones.

You could not rob us, though we forgot.
You could not erase us, though we could not write.
You could not silence, though we could not speak.
The stories, the laughter, the moments that passed
Into their keep, you could not steal
Into a night of silence.

Look at me, Alzheimer's.
My life is restored, remembered, reconstructed,
With tools of love, dignity and laughter.
A house of memories is built
By my children, and their children
For generations to come.

So here I am, Alzheimer's,
With family, friends, and loved ones.
What you thought you stole
Is still here. We are all still here.
So Alzheimer's,
What do you think of that? ❧

Revist
RED SLIDER

Come in, my dear, if you must;
it was inevitable that we meet this way,
was it not? You look so well and I,
but no matter if we are strangers
meeting like this face-to-face,
we have met before, on the steps
to reach this place, have we not?
Of course we have, though
I've never seen you before, have I?
Still, we are together, you and I,
All our lives we circle one another,
exchanging small favors along the way,
Do we not? Do we not? Of course
we don't! I've never seen you before.
I'm quite sure. Yes, now I'm quite sure. ❧

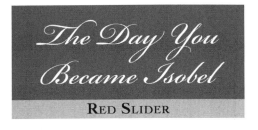

The Day You Became Isobel
RED SLIDER

Not on the days you lost your
keys,
or the words you couldn't quite
recall,
or the puzzles unsolved in the
Sunday *Times*;

nor, when the refrigerator got lost,
or the steps home unretracable,
or the faces of your children unrecognized.

It was on the day I returned to your name
for the sake of my memory as much as yours.
I said, "Isobel," to remember the you of you,
and whenever I spoke about you to them,
or to myself about you; or called out to you,
"Isobel, it's time for lunch. Isobel, I'm here."

That was the day you become so much more
than the ghost of a "changed person,"
a "she was" stuck in my native thought;
more than that, so much more than "Mom." ✺

Spring in Autumn

FRANCES KAKUGAWA

*They are still here, oh, they are still here.
These conversations with Alzheimer's
patients gave me as much pleasure as
any social exchange at a cocktail party.*

Are they the last leaves of
Autumn?

John

"You have a beautiful smile."
His eyes, cloudless blue
Look into mine
Daring me to believe him.

I offer him my face.
"Does that come with a kiss?"
For one brief moment
He responds to a flirt.

I feel his kiss on my cheek.
We share a smile.
For that brief moment,
A smile between two strangers,
A man and a woman.
We prolong our smile
Till his caregiver
Comes for him.

Are they the last leaves of Autumn,
Aimlessly falling for that last bonfire?

Gambatte, Kakugawa-San

It is her last day at adult day care.
She is held erect by the caregiver.
"This is Mrs. K's last day with us.
She is going to the health day care
Beginning tomorrow."

A moan fills the room.
Do they know the significance
Of this move, that her ability
To walk and to use the bathroom
Has diminished? Will they soon be next?

Spontaneously they sing two Japanese children's songs
And "You are My Sunshine."

Their voices surpass any rehearsed chorale.
One patient quietly stands, walks to a box of Kleenex.
She hands a tissue to my mother
And uses one for her eyes.
Shouts of "Gambatte, Be Strong, Kakugawa-san,
Goodbye"
Fill the room while a few nod in sleep.
I take my mother's hand and lead her out of the room.
Shouts of "Gambatte" follow us
As I search for my own tissue.

The purity of their childlike farewell
Spills over and over
As I drive my mother home.

Mrs. H

She walks out of the bathroom
Just as I am walking my mother in.
Her blouse hanging over her slacks,
She looks at me.
"Is there another way I can wear this blouse?
I notice you always dress nicely.
Can you help me look like you?"

This is her first response to me
In all the months I've seen her.
Alzheimer's had stolen from her, too.

I show her three ways to wear her blouse.
She prefers the first where I tied her blouse
In a knot at her waistband.
She walks back into the bathroom,
Slowly pirouettes before the mirror.
"Yes," she says, "You are smart. I look better."
I nod, one woman to another.

Patrick

We meet for the first time,
McDonald's breakfast before us.
His shy smile and strong handshake
Tell me he knows I am there,
A new face in his home.

He silently eats his eggs and rice
While his caregiver-wife and I chat.
After my second cup of coffee,
He looks straight into my eyes:
"Are you married?"

"No, Patrick, I'm not married.
Nobody wants to marry me.
Don't you think that's terrible?"
He smiles and conceals a chuckle.
His wife adds, "But Patrick, she had many lovers."
He looks at me, smiles and deliberately says,

"Good for you."
After breakfast he is handed his cane
As he slowly tries to find his seat in the living room.
He spreads the morning papers before his face
Leaving us to savor our third cup of coffee.

After our fourth, I take his hand
And bid him goodbye,
"Patrick, it was good to meet you.
I'll come again to see you."

He returns my handshake with a clear, "Good."
I saunter out, sated with womanhood
For all the right things said to me
By this man who still knows
What it is to be a man.

Are they the last leaves of Autumn?
Or is there still a river flowing
Somewhere deep within? ❦

Thief

FRANCES KAKUGAWA

Before the thief came
I saw her with all the flaws of an
imperfect mother.
I became righteous and judgmental
In my quiet, unspoken perception of her.

Then the thief came quietly into the night
Like that fog on little cat feet
And slowly began to rob her
Of what was rightfully hers since her birth.

Childhood memories,
Dates and places.
Yesterdays and todays,
Even family faces.
Oh so quietly, so silently
Stolen without a sound.

The mother is no longer here,
But a shell of a woman,
Leaving me nothing to judge, nothing at all.
She sits for hours without a past, without a present,
A woman struggling each day to retain
What little dignity the thief had not found
In the tiny remaining crevices of her mind.

My heart aches with love
For the woman she has become.
Perhaps there is a reason for this thief
A final transformation of a mother
Into her purest form,
A newborn babe once again
Before her final journey. ৺

Pulling down the window shade
of page, pink emery board pressed
beneath her fingers, she reveals
each line, each line unraveled,

The Reading Specialist

RED SLIDER

each undeciphered word, pure sound,
ripples of phoneme without meaning
crackle on the dry parchment.

"It's from, I think it's from, my
daughter,"

she says, "she's having a baby."
"They'll come and show me, maybe
tomorrow." But the secret of spring,
so many springs ago, is caught in the crease
on the blue page with the little yellow flowers,
worn through from too many years of renewal.

Desperately, she tries to refold
the torn halves of faded event;
but, too late; the sounds spill
their vacant contents onto the floor.
For a moment, recognition catches
in her throat. Then, voiceless,
the parchment shudders…erasing.

Around the dining room table
They sit silently in wheelchairs
Waiting for the dinner cart.

The Equalizer
FRANCES KAKUGAWA

I look at my mother,
Who rose each morning
Hours before sunrise
To wait on the back steps
For the van to take her
To the flower farm.
Until age eighty-five she packed
Thousands of vanda orchids a day,
A job she delighted in
Until the day of her diagnosis.

I look at the others gathered around the table
And wonder. Was one a CEO? A farmer?
A surgeon? A clerk ? A dancer?
I want to shout, "What were you?"
It makes not an inch of difference.
They are still men and women
Holding on rightfully to who they are,
Waiting for their plastic trays. ❧

A fully bloomed gardenia
Sends such fragrance of sensual pleasure
From each unfolded petal.

Gardenia

FRANCES KAKUGAWA

A woman, concealed in silence
Was once, too, in her own realm
Of such flitting glory.

Dressmaker

    Drafting and sewing,

    Pumping away at her machine,

    Singing songs

    Now Japanese oldies,

    She dressed the people

    Of her village.

Girl Scout

    The first Girl Scout leader

    To organize and uniform

    The young lasses of her village,

    A maverick in her own time

    Joining communities

    Between unpaved dirt roads.

Dancer

    At PTA meetings,

    The first on the dance floor

    Led by plantation managers.

    Active and vivacious,

    At *bon* dances, a dancer,

    On Buddhist grounds.

A Surrogate Mother

    A young GI, far from home,

    Nostalgic for his own mother's Italian kitchen,

    Dined on spaghetti sauce and pasta

    In our kitchen of plantation means

    Before being shipped out

    To foreign battlefields after December 7.

Bi-Linguist

    President of her Buddhist Women's Club,

    Giving speeches in Japanese and English,

    The best trump card player

    Among men and women,

    Expletives to match

    Any sailor's tongue.

Therapist

    The confidential therapist

    Lending an ear

    To the young men and women

    Who gathered at her sewing machine.

    A treasure box of intimate love stories

    Never to be shared.

It is not the spotted brown petals of the gardenia

But what it was in its splendor

That will become its final image. ❧

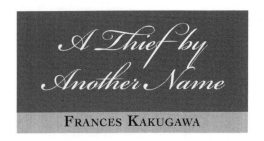

A Thief by Another Name

FRANCES KAKUGAWA

It was the most exhilarating feeling
When at age sixteen I got the key
To the family car and drove solo
All over town through traffic lights
To country roads and back to home
Where trust was given with license.
Since then, each time I fit that key
Into the ignition and turn it right,
And hear the hum of the engine,
I get to relive that same golden moment
Of seventy years ago.

A moment of complete freedom
As I take complete control of a vehicle,
Freedom to turn right or to left,
Freedom to exceed the speed limit or otherwise.
So many decisions, decisions I am able to make
Because with this key, I am also given
My own dignity! My own capability!
My own manhood! My independence!
With no one telling me
What to do, where to go, how to go.

What exhilaration!
To be the owner of that one key.
The wonder of this freedom
Is one needs to be alone.

One passenger, just one passenger
Takes half of this freedom away.
The AC, speed limit, routes to different places,
They all become half of yours,
When there is but one passenger.
Ah yes, one needs to be alone
Alone behind the wheel.
With a tank full of gas
And somewhere to go.
Today my keys were taken from me. ✻

The Pen

I was but a child
When I wrote my first line of poetry
That senselessly rhymed.
It would be my ticket
Out of God-forsaken Kapoho:
A ticket away from kerosene lamps,
Outhouses, battery-run radios.
And Pidgin English.
I believed it would be my ticket
To Greenwich Village, New York City,
Paris and Stockholm, Sweden.
Little did I know
That poetry would help me conquer
That debilitating disease, Alzheimer's.
Way before those men and women in white
In laboratory sanctions.

If you want the truth when you ask a caregiver, "Did you have a good night's sleep?" or "How are you doing? How's your wife (or dad) doing?" you may need to sit for an hour or two for your answer. Sometimes, what appears to be the simplest of tasks becomes the most time consuming, even a trip to the store or the lacing of a shoelace. And a day off from caregiving is not so easily taken. We have become so conditioned as caregivers that we may need days to reprogram ourselves to adjust to a day of freedom.

Our 24-Hour Day
DAYS & NIGHTS IN THE LIVES OF LOVED ONES & THEIR CAREGIVERS

·CHAPTER THREE·

Caregivers' writing is not a place for mere complaints or a calendar of daily happenings. Sometimes it may seem that way, but writing gives a caregiver the freedom to express their innermost thoughts and the space to find the divine in the experience. The caregivers here take you into their uncensored thoughts and feelings as the physical aspects of caring are being attended to, at home, in public, nursing facilities and in doctors' offices or in hospitals. It was a challenging place to be—there is pure exhaustion, anger, rage, feelings of hopelessness, hope and joy—but at the end of the day, there was always reflection and the knowledge that above everything else that was going on, human dignity and compassion had to be preserved. These are the stories that remain untold when caregivers are asked, "How are you?" and they're expected to say, "I'm okay." ✒

And the Winner Is...

FRANCES KAKUGAWA

"How is your mother?" has turned into "How are you?"s
Where automated responses are given without thought.
Yesterday at the mailboxes,
An acquaintance asked once again,
"How's your mother?"
"My mother?" I said.
"I think she is the prettiest woman
On the entire fifth floor and if they ran a beauty contest
For the elderly, I would enter her and I know she'd win."

She looked at me in discomfort as if to say,
"I wanted you to just say, 'Fine.'"

Half-past three, in camera

I awake and lay on the mat checking the vague need I had to pee. Checking the tense. Not sufficient to normally arouse me but I decide I will try anyway. So I roll off the mat and go to the next room and relieve myself in the dark. Just as I thought, not enough to bother. But my sense of "bother" is no longer mine. The return to the bedroom is blazed with unfocused eyes, registered in a slightly darker shadow over the pitch black of the living room. Something there is less visible than the fabric of darkness. Mom? I check my question. The barely discernible shape is perceptibly denser against the regular lines of the sofa. Doesn't move. Should it? I check my senses. Her hand in mine, I can now unwrap her from the heavy Indian knit blanket with the other, taking care not to squeeze anything at all as she no longer tolerates even the slightest intrusion, the least ambient pressure. It is all that is left of her defense system—the gentlest touch, a potential killing blow.

Nightbook #1

RED SLIDER

Half-past three, with searchlight

Even so, she warns from somewhere in the lightless muddle, Don't hurt me! I check my defenses. Mom, I'd never hurt you. But I know I do, a hundred times every day. Pouring her hand into the sleeve of her robe, patting her on the shoulder after pushing the chair up to the table, a sock-snag on a toenail (and when, I wince, should I treat her to the agony of cutting them?) A simple difference, the gradient a couple of molecules make scurrying one way or the other over open skin registers like a shard of ice drilled through her chest, my fingers just grazing her throat throws her head back against the chair, the last button on her blouse is lost and I will have to start over.

Half-past three-oh-one

Mom? What are you doing sitting here? A rhetorical question: a probe for a phrase of bewilderment. More often, now, just the guest whimper of consciousness. I make approach noises, intone the prowl of bears at the margins of a campsite, to have her stand up. She answers with a short moan, a faint foghorn signal in muddle so thick one cannot even see the mental images inside their own minds. Awake and lost, I think to myself, "Log it." I press the "jungle gym" of my forearm against her as familiar prehensile reflexes take over. Frail hands grasp the bar of my arm. Pull yourself up, Pull! We do "The Lift" together, ignoring everything but the exact forces needed to slowly raise her to her feet. Too little grasp or too much pull by fractions of an ounce and we'll lose it and have to start over. It is a successful maneuver this time as I slip my arm around her waist like a safety bar and walk her back up the hall toward her bedroom.

Three-twenty-seven at half-past three-oh-two

What I don't know is whether she got lost before or after the hall outside the bathroom directly across from her bedroom. And if she got to the bathroom, did she recognize the toilet? And if she recognized it, did she know what to do? And if she did, did she even remember what she got up to go there and do in the first place? Probably not. I do a quick check of the toilet as we reach that end of the hall, synched in what I call "her Chinese steps." A small piece of tissue with other evidence of use. The tissue from before? I can't recall. Mom, do you have to pee-pee? The juvenilia come easy. At first they masked the breach of realms; personal function with diminutive innocence. Then it covered the recognition of breach with immediate distractions, silly humor and sounds regressive. Finally, a natural vocabulary that is all that is left of recognition. Clinical terms don't register at all anymore; normal usage sets off a panic of trying to recall meanings that refuse to identify themselves. "Pee-pee" and "poop" it is.

Half-past three on three-fifty

After that, I don't know, we're not quite there yet. Sometimes it's just plain instinct. I have kids somewhere, she might say. Her hand moves uncertainly, I check tenses, across her chest, down her hips, she pulls at her pant legs. Oh, you need to pee? (I know how I knew what her gesture meant the second time, but how did I know how to translate that the first time?) You're talking too fast, I don't understand. I adjust the pace by half a minute: You need to pee-pee? Maybe, toilet? Pee-pee? Oh, yes, I think so. Soon the whole matter (by instinct) will be managed by instinct alone. For now I'm just thankful that she can hold her crotch and look around for something she should be doing. Thankful for that, and Depends.

An hour past three

It is done. We make it to the bed without further excursion. I pull the warmth of the electric blanket over her. I will need to get her up early and take her to "school." The installation of the new heatpump will require inside duct work as well. It is not her regular day care day but the confusion would disturb great swatches of molecule, diffuse them into the noise of passing workmen, hoist them from cranes lowering three-and-a-half tons of cube onto the roof, smear them under boots over sagging rafters. It is enough to watch minute amounts of her leak out into the vapor of rattling breakfast dishes and the sequence of steps from first light to first shoe, gone forever into the vacuum of life. She enjoys watching the million dollar quiz. Right or wrong, the questions and answers are a continuous stream of nonsense. The money is nonsense. But the refusal to answer a question, the confession of emptiness, that she understands. She cheers the confessor. She is satisfied to see them handed a check for not having an answer. She asks how she can get on that program.

Half-past three-oh-five

My acquired mother antennae do a bed check in the dim light. I will need to stay for awhile until she is drifting. Otherwise, she will be up again in ten or fifteen minutes. Loneliness is driving her tonight. It doesn't go away, it is merely overcome. I rest my hand lightly on her shoulder and we fall into a regular breathing pattern—I suppress my own consumptive hacking. It works. Five minutes later I get up and go back to bed.

Half-past three, en molé

I laugh as I roll onto the hard mats between bouts of wheezing, apnea, hacking and deciding whether to peel my socks off my gout-bloated shins and expose them to the relief of the arctic temperatures in my room. Hell, I'm sicker than she is. Sicker, poorer, crazier, more forgetful (What does she have to remember?), depressed, lonely, numb, depersonalized and flat out burned out. I laugh again. Grief? Ah yes, the thing that's stuck somewhere between "laugh" and "laugh." My friend's words, the ones he sent me after burying his father, run through my head as I roll on my back and wait for the day's nicotine toxemia to settle down. He talked about the "grail of pain" and I think, there isn't a one of us in the bunch—friends, wives or passersby—who hasn't asked him for a prescription at one time or another. I turn over and get up. "Nightbook" waits in the workroom like a dense shadow...

6 a.m.

Soon she will be standing in the kitchen, just off this workroom. She will be completely confused. The lights from there, the dark in there, the table, chairs, a clock, the stove pot will all be strangers. I stop and go to her. She says, "Let's go home now." I am relieved that she still recognizes me. I will answer, "Today is a school day. I'll put on some fresh coffee and Miles Davis and then we'll get you dressed and ready." "Oh good," she replies, "I want to go to school now." ✣

Caregiver Bio

· S E T S U K O Y O S H I D A ·

Setsuko "Sets" Yoshida was a registered nurse for thirty-three years in Honolulu, Hawai'i when her husband Yoshio "Patrick" Yoshida (1916–2000) was diagnosed. Patrick served in the 442nd Regimental Combat Team in Europe during World War II and saw friends perish in battle. The experience was a time in his life that he didn't discuss with others. He worked as the executive secretary at the Mō'ili'li Community Center and later as a realtor. Sets was the first to open an AIDS unit in Hawai'i at Queen's Hospital and was honored for her work with the Award for Compassionate Care from the Life Foundation in 1986. She now resides in New York City with her son and his companion.

I am awakened abruptly from a deep sleep
At 2:30 a.m.
By the sound of a waterfall.

Night Watch
SETSUKO YOSHIDA

In the dim night light
I discern the silhouette of a man
Standing and urinating on the carpeted floor
Between two chest of drawers.

I jump out of bed shouting,
"What are you doing?
This is the bedroom
Not the bathroom!"

The blank forlorn look on his face
Sends a message of emptiness.
He does not know where he is,
Nor what is happening
To make me so upset.

I guide him into the shower,
Spray the lower half of his body
With warm water,
Towel dry him and
"Harness" him with Depends,
Not giving him a choice, this time.

I tuck him into bed and
He promptly falls asleep
Like a newborn babe.

Meanwhile, I'm on the floor
With a new roll of Chelsea paper towels
Soaking up the urine
From the carpeted floor.

In the silence of the night
I am struck by
A moment of sadness and helplessness.
"Wow!" there is nothing else for me to do
But clean up this mess!

"With repeated practice
You'll get used to it,"
I hear a caregiver say.

The question for me is
Will I? Will I? Ever?
Be able to accept all this
With serenity
In the midst of my suffering? ༄

The time clock of my mind
Awakens me at 5:30 a.m.
He is sleeping soundly like a child
On top of the bed,

The lower half in his birthday suit.

Do It

SETSUKO YOSHIDA

Peeking into the bathroom
I react in horror!
BM all over the vinyl floor,
Toilet seat and wastebasket!

Inhaling and exhaling deeply
And telling myself
To live in the present moment,
To forget the self,
To single-mindedly immerse myself
To clean up the mess.

Opening wide the jalousie windows
In the bathroom and bedroom
Allows the brisk cool trade winds to dissipate the odor.
No need to spray Lysol Mountain Air scent,
I put on the disposable vinyl gloves,
Get a bucket of vinegar water and rags,
Go on my hands and knees
And start cleaning one area at a time.

Emptying my mind of any thought
I follow what Nike says
"Just do it!" ✼

Caregiver Bio

·MARY SWISHER·

Mary Swisher, a photographer and writer, lives in Sacramento with her husband Bob (1930–), a former physician. Bob loves to sing to the hits of the oldies so if you visit, be ready to sing along with him. Mary is the principal photographer of *Architectural Terra Cotta of Gladding, McBean* (Windgate Press, 1989), a featured photographer in *Presidio Gateways*, (Chronicle Books, 1994) and author-photographer of an art book, *The Stones of Mani: Views of The Southern Peloponnese* (Stalwart Press, 1999). Her work is included in collections throughout the United States, Europe and Japan. Mary is finding the balancing act of being an artist and a caretaker for her husband an ever-changing challenge. However, through attending writing workshops with Frances, she has come to see caregiving as something other than a burden—it is an act of love.

Hot water bottle in place
head placed into feathery pillow
ready for oblivion or dreams
I float out on my raft…

Falling Asleep

MARY SWISHER

but no, is the chicken house door
shut?
I roll over, he said he shut the
door, but no,
maybe that was yesterday he shut the door and he sleeps now.
Was it yesterday he found the hen dead
beneath the roost, frozen?

Sleep and sleep I want to sleep but that last chicken
is now in my head resting on her downy relatives
The rats overhead are quiet
The poison worked…they all bled to death
Who is eating their bodies to meet their death?
I am a mass murderer!
A screech owl will drop down our chimney to confirm this.

Sleep and more sleep, I want sleep
tomorrow I have the list:
"doctor, market, post office, pick up prescription"…no, cancel that…
wait, I forgot…what did I forget?
The cat wants out or maybe he wants to be fed
no, he's rolling on the bed full of play.

I just want to go away soon,
a tropical island, a hammock
swinging in the breeze where….
Now he wakes up and says he is mad at me
then he and the cat go to sleep.
I can hear them sleep, infuriating sleep!
Public Radio comes on, it's 3 a.m.
my hot water bottle is cold,
and day break is sleepless hours away. ✒

She's in the other room, feeding herself. You need to realize this is an accomplishment worthy of an Olympic gold medal. It begins with lacing a boot or taping a wrist or taking a warm-up lap or drawing to an inside straight.

Six months ago I was barely able to feed her. A bad reaction to a new medication lit her up like the sun and dropped her like a limp rag doll. Now she can hold a spoon by herself, in signature sim-ian fashion, and put away her favorite foods with the gusto of an athlete in training. This was not supposed to be, when you realize Alzheimer's victims cannot learn anything new. The mind peels itself away like an onion until only the peel and the whir of the garbage disposal remain. The residue, where the action ought to be, is simply tangles of plaque and fused wiring hopelessly burnt to a cinder. But she did learn and from God knows what reserve. It won't last forever, but for now it's impossible not to begin each morning with the sense there's a torch bearer in the background clearing the tunnel and igniting the flame. In the distance, there is the daily call: "LET THE GAMES BEGIN." ✒

1

She tied that bow
with such perfect concentration,
pulling the loop around

The Last Olympiad

RED SLIDER

the index, saddling the
bitter end,
done at last when she'd
coaxed

the lace over the arthritic arch
on her bony finger,
and finished the job

with a tug
and a grunt.

2

A blue sneaker waves a happy foot
in triumph. The flaming arrow of Olympus,
her cane, taut as a bow,
the torchlight shining from her eyes.

I'm ready to go, she says on the final lap
to the door. "Not quite," I say
as I hand her the other shoe
for her grueling decathlon.

Today, a silver medal performance,
tomorrow, who knows, perhaps
her buttons will be done correctly? ✒

1.

My father is in his second year of Alzheimer's.
Like a butterfly I escaped my house today.
Lately, I've raced away at every opportunity

Just to pretend that my life is
normal again.
There's a desperation about it,
Like the brief mating life of a

termite.

2.

Sometimes I resist deep thinking
And can no longer remember my dreams.
My identity—who I really am
Is buried under layers of sand.
Sometimes an occasional dream
Will remind me of how this tiny voice
Has been brutalized into submission
So that I could be the best caregiver I can.

3.

Being true to that Little Voice,
I recognize myself as a creative wild spirit,
Limitless as an ocean.
A woman who longs to feel attractive again
Rather than invisible.
So I race away from the house
Leaving the hired caregiver with my father,

So I can go out into the world
And find myself again
In all-too-short experiments of freedom.

4.

My father is in his fifth year of Alzheimer's
He has a terrible cough now.
I have to puree all his food.
It takes me one hour each morning
To slowly and tenderly perform the
Cleaning and toileting ritual.
Encouraging him as I would a baby
So he knows who I am
And that everything's all right.
He's always happy to see me.
Every single morning it's the same
Twists, stretches, aches, reaches, pushes and pulls.
When I wake up my thoughts are,
"Gotta clean Daddy up, poor thing."
Any chance of remembering a dream is gone.
The habit of putting myself last
Has become second nature.

5.

Someone in my support group said,
"A thing is not truly done unless it's done with love."
She didn't remember who said it.
If I don't practice this with Daddy every day

In the mundane daily rituals.
I would surely be overcome with depression.
In the moment
Actions of love
Calm us both together.

6.

My father is in his seventh year of Alzheimer's.
I've been with him every step of the journey,
An intimacy no one would want,
But that has come with gifts and blessings.
My touch on his skin is as gentle as a butterfly.
His well-being is as fragile as a butterfly.
I toil to preserve the dust on his spirit wings
So he can flutter into the beautiful light
Seamlessly and in peace. ✤

Eugenie "Genie" Mitchell was a caregiver for her mother, Joyce Johnson Mitchell (1928–2011), a homemaker, master gardener and gentle spirit whose proudest accomplishment was that she raised four children, each very different from the others. Joyce received a preliminary diagnosis of Alzheimer's disease in 1998 and continued to live independently, although with increasing assistance and support, for five years before she and Genie moved in together for the remainder of Joyce's life. Genie is a former legal aid lawyer who, as Joyce's needs grew, eventually stopped working to care for Joyce fulltime. Of having her daughter as her caregiver, Joyce said she never knew she could feel such gratitude, and yet such resentment, at the same time. Genie did not know that she could experience such challenge, such tedium and such exhaustion at the same time, but learned that she was capable of love in action. Genie now works as an administrative law judge and still lives in the home she shared with her mother in Sacramento, California.

I am the *torero*.

I hold not a cape, but her coat,
    a bright French blue

              instead of Spanish red.

The Bullfighter

EUGENIE MITCHELL

         I regard my other.
          Slight and vulnerable,
she is animated, talking silly and senseless.
Or, she is silent and absent.

I hold her coat
    off to my left
    for my *paso*
    to her right.

I move the sleeve toward its position.
I follow her restless right arm.
I feint slightly to her left
    drawing her toward me.
Quickly, I reverse,
    pushing the sleeve
    toward her arm again.

Her arm mimics my moves,
    but remains out of reach.
Eluded.
A failed *faena*.

Thus we commence our *toreador* dance.
 I am following her arm,
 and she is following mine.

Blue cloth outstretched between us,
 we circle and circle
 in our own *pasodoble*.
I am the torero.

But I am not the *matador*.
And she is not a bull. ✤

SETSUKO YOSHIDA

Assumptions and expectations
Of what he can and should do
Must be erased from my mind.
An inner voice reminds me,
"Be more sensitive and understanding."

His trousers, T-shirt
And long-sleeved flannel shirt
Are placed side by side on top of the bed.
He turns them around and around
Examining them closely.
Not knowing the difference
Between front and back
He wears his T-shirt reversed,

And inside out at times.
When buttoning his flannel shirt,
The buttons are not in alignment
With the buttonholes.

While cooking breakfast,
I look towards the hallway.
He has walked out of the bedroom
Through the hallway to the dining room.

He is standing beside the chair
Wearing his shirt and boxer shorts only,
Thinking he is properly dressed
To sit at the table to eat his meal.

He looks like a little boy.
His innocence is so revealing
It warms my heart.
I smile, and tell him
What he has forgotten to wear.
He looks at my face and chuckles
As a glimmer of awareness dawns.

Together, we put on his khaki trousers
Embraced in the centerless circle
Of Boundless Life. ❧

I hate Costco.
Cavernous assault on our senses,
dangerous decibels and fluorescence,
caustic reek of hotdog essence —

gargantuous consumption is its
quintessence.

EUGENIE MITCHELL   Hefty, beefy families of five,
moon-faces ballooning over
            loads of chips
            and fifty rolls
            of toilet tissue —
the Costco lesson is just this:
excess becomes
excrement.

And yet we take the bait —
            six tens of Depends
            six dollars less,
and here we are,
cart crammed with cartons
lime and pink
in lurid proclamation
of our own excretion.

Next we navigate ironically,
the cleanly row of godly laundry,
stocking up in triplicate,

Clorox bottles in a box,
forty-plus pounds
of rigorous wrangling.
I struggle and sweat, then find success —
only to lose…
my mom.

Invisible I
while bent with bleach,
so too did she
disappear from view.
Is she plodding along, trailing only the tide?
Or has a dimpled infant lured her aside?
Maybe she's made for the exit,
ever unerring destination
despite her disorientation.

I shout her name down every lane,
disturbing the massive multitudes
into silent aversion,
their meditations transcended
by my intrusion —
but all to no avail.

Afraid to foray
in the parking lot,
and afraid to not,
I teeter at the door

where the checkers listen
to my description
and send a signal
throughout the store.

She is all field-mark,
          as the birders say,
hair white as any bald eagle's pate,
her plumage a coat of sage,
with purple pants
and bells atinkle on her toes.
Though arrayed so vividly,
she is but a little titmouse
among these giant predators.
I fear...No. I check myself.
I had better hope
she is not their prey.

Fighting the blinding red rise
of plain old panic —
Stay calm!
What to do?
Think!
But not of evil!

How could I lose her?
Stupid Clorox!
Bad daughter!

Move! Move!
Do something!
What?

I finally espy her white hair's crest,
bobbing slowly
in the teeming sea of being.
She emerges in pure purple,
green coat a wad in her arms.

The relief of reunion is only mine:
Mom is fine.
For her, there is
nothing not normal:
she never knows her whereabouts.

Now I propel our bounty to purchase,
        clenching her arm to my side,
        pretending to be her escort,
As we resume our unstately, glacial parade
to the checkstand, our last resort.

The line is long, Mom is tired.
She does not understand the line idea.
She loudly proclaims
that she does not know my name,
and why should she do what I say?
The multitudes no longer look away.

Antsy in the crush at the door,
      Mom feels trapped,
        wants out, out, with urgency.
Receipt checked perfunctorily,
I rush the cart outside the door,
but Mom…
sits down on the floor.

And will not rise.
      Stretching out her legs,
      crossing her ankles,
she is blissfully defiant,
ignorant of the masses
bottlenecking behind her.

They glare at me.
Disdainful of my helplessness,
they think she is injured
and that I am mean.
They think I am stupid to cajole.
They offer her lifts,
and can't understand
when she resists.

I plead. I try to lead her.
I just want to leave.
I hate Costco.

Oh, floor, drop open!
Swallow me whole!
Oh, Scotty, beam me up!
Make it stop!
Cure this disease!

Kindly young nurse intercedes,
helps me hoist her,
atilt, to her feet
and walks us into the setting sun,
where Mom exclaims,
"We've been having fun!"

I still hate Costco.

For now I envy her oblivion?

I hate Costco. ༄

When I try holding on to her arm
As we walk the mall at Ala Moana Center:
"Let go! Let go! You're hurting me!" she yells.
Passersby stare at the abuser.

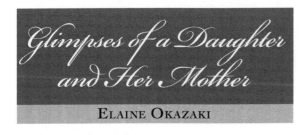

Glimpses of a Daughter and Her Mother

ELAINE OKAZAKI

She's never one to walk
with me.
She's legally blind, you
know
So she walks behind me

As we stroll down the mall.

I turn to look behind.
She's turning into Penney's.
Quickly, I touch her arm
To lead her back.

"You're a witch! You're a witch!"
She rants and raves.
In just a second...
Everyone stops to stare
At the abused and the abuser. ❧

Down the escalator of Macy's, she stands
Behind me and remarks,
"Your white hair is sticking out!"
This from my mother

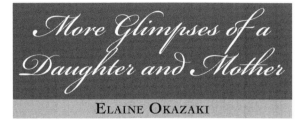

More Glimpses of a Daughter and Mother

ELAINE OKAZAKI

Diagnosed legally blind
by her physician.

Walking behind me along
the aisle of Costco,
She suddenly squeezes

my side at the waist
And snaps, "What's this?"
Then her hand grabs the other side.
She remarks loudly, "They're on both sides!"
The Sprint agent roars with laughter.
But I'm not laughing...

The Handi-Van arrives for her usual pickup.
"C'mon, Mom, your bus is here."
"Let it wait," she retorts. And she slowly sits down.
Finally, my husband tells her to hurry up
And not to keep the driver waiting, his voice, a bit gruff.
She turns to walk toward the door and mutters to him,
"I'll deal with you when I come back!"

Is she the mom who nurtured me?
Is it the dementia playing havoc with my mind?
Or is this really my mom? I don't know. ❦

Illnesses have turned me into a sleuth.

A self-appointed detective

With agenda in hand, and without your consent

I write letters to your doctors.

Covert Activities

LINDA NAGATA

I call your doctors.

Ask questions. Get information.

Research additional information.

Heart attacks, bypass surgeries, and cancer lend themselves

To this scientific attack. I can deal with those.

There are things to do.

A plan to follow, and always hope for a cure.

Alzheimer's leaves me tilting at windmills.

Nothing to be done.

No plan to follow.

No hope. No cure.

I am powerless.

I turn in my badge. ✀

I can hardly wait till Monday!
Every minute of every weekend,
my friend Monday
beckons ahead.

Requiem for Monday

EUGENIE MITCHELL

Monday's my goal;
Monday, my salvation!

Monday is the day I'm free!
Free!
Free to get myself clean!

Free to do things for me!
Free to do my list of deeds!
Free to read, and read!

Monday, I can go outside!
Monday, I can drive!
    drive wherever I like!
Monday, I can make my own meal!
Monday, I can eat it in peace.

Monday morning comes,
my anticipation at its peak.
I rush through Mom's ablutions.
I seat her on the bus.

Now my time arrives.
After bidding Mom bye-bye,
I re-enter our abode,

and in that very moment,
my motivation takes its leave of me.

My mind ceases its imaginings.
It becomes a desert,
lonely and dry.

I get as far as putting on the bottom sheet,
        before I wear out, sit down and stare,
        uncomprehending, at a magazine.

I start the wash, but computer-dazed,
        I ignore demands of timers beeping;
        no mere machine can animate me.

Breakfast dishes half-washed.
Linen closet doors agape.
Bathroom, toothbrush-strewn.
Watering can in repose
        part-way round the room.
One phone call maybe made,
        but my list otherwise untended.

I don't jump in the bath,
or make myself lunch.
I don't go outside,
no invigorating top-down ride.
The novel I'm into no longer appeals.

On Mondays, no friends call;
only creditors do.
They're all revving up.
Their workweek's beginning.
The only revolutions in my life
are hands circling the clock.

Cuckoo!
Unrelentingly.
Cuckoo! Cuckoo!
I am wasting the time of my life.
Cuckoo! Cuckoo! Cuckoo!
I can't wake myself up.

Cuckoo! Cuckoo! Cuckoo! Cuckoo!
Am I crazy? Or is it exhaustion?
Just pointless procrastination?
My self-exhortations don't provoke me to action—
is it a character flaw, a moral dereliction?
Or an ADD symptom?
Or depression, or both?

Cuckoo! Cuckoo! Cuckoo! Cuckoo! Cuckoo!
Now, Mom will be home
        sometime soon.
So when will I finally
        live here, too?

(Maybe Wednesday.) ✺

Sometimes
When I'm sitting in the living room,
I'm suddenly filled with unexplainable joy,
Joy that begins from deep within

Joy

FRANCES KAKUGAWA

And slowly seeks its way toward
every pore
Of my body that has become one
With sadness, hopelessness,
Fear and pure exhaustion.
How can this be,
This overwhelming surge of joy
That leaves room for nothing else
When my mother
Is sitting here in the same room,
Silently studying her hands,
Occasionally turning, turning
Her opal ring on her ring finger?
How can I be filled with such pure joy
When the presence of my mother
Reminds me of why we are both here?
What can it be except for
The presence of God,
Whispering, "I am here."
I weep tears of joy
For the two of us. ✤

The Power of Ink

I can't let it die.
Once I let its grasp on me
Loosen and uncoil, it will die
And I can't let it happen.
If it dies,
Generations of my people
From Hiroshima to Hawai'i…
My grandparents, great-grandparents I never met
My mother whose life I held with honor as I
Helped her live her last Alzheimer's life.
They will all die,
Erasing all memories
From the slate of their children, grandchildren
And all future children.
I can't let it die.

What will I get from writing? What will my loved one get from my taking time out to write?

Writing doesn't eliminate any of the realities of caregiving: the medical, health care issues, the daily changes in our loved ones' behavior and our total exhaustion. Time runs into years; plans we had for our own lives are changed; there is emotional and physical toll; we grieve, seeing the slow disappearance of a loved one.

Caregiver Into Poet-Caregiver

· CHAPTER FOUR ·

No, writing doesn't eliminate nor lessen any of these realities but it allows us to go beyond these curtains that tend to suffocate us. Writing can become a magnifying glass that forces us to examine what is there—a pause button to stop us in the middle of chaos in order to find some meaning and to make sense of what's happening.

Setsuko Yoshida, who was in my first caregivers' writing group, questioned the writing process at first. In her poem, "Can I?" (page 104), she asks, "Anger, resentment and frustrations / Overwhelm me at unexpected moments…How can I deal with such feelings and thoughts?" As she explored her feelings through writing, she came to accept the reality of what it meant to be a caregiver for her husband. Sets' poems helped her find solace in her Buddhist beliefs, as seen in her poem, "Reality" (page 110).

Writing gives us permission to speak the truth of how we feel and think. When we release this truth, there is less residue left for future guilt and remorse. In my poems "Oscar Time" (page

112) and "Unspoken Mornings" (page 113) I speak of wanting caregiving to end. Only in art form, can I say this with out the fear of being spiritually punished, because the reality is that for caregiving to end, my mother has to die. In a poem, we have the freedom to say such a thing without guilt.

Writing gives us a creative tool to re-examine the reality before us and to find new meaning and understanding. When my mother was first diagnosed with Alzheimer's, she began to sign her name in a composition tablet. "So shame," she said, "If I went to the bank and forgot to sign my name." Toward the end of her disease, she had filled five composition books with her signature. I first dismissed it as one of her strange behaviors brought on by Alzheimer's. When I looked at it from a different perspective, as a poet-caregiver, her act transformed from one of strangeness to one of my mother trying to retain her own identity and self. My own poem, "Five Notebooks" (page 115), taught me something about compassion and respect for the disease and for my mother.

Writing can also help us discover ourselves. In time, your writing will speak back to you. It will tell you about what you are feeling and thinking, it will make a space in the busy life of caregiving for you to make sense of what you and your loved one are doing. It clears a time for you to reflect, gain insights and affirm the dignity and respect that you and your loved ones share with one another. One woman came to a workshop, complaining of her mother. "She pushes my button on purpose to just get me angry." But the poem she wrote spoke of her love for her mother. She seemed surprised at the emotion she was displaying. "Writing helped you find your own voice," I told her. "This is you, this loving, compassionate person." She stood up and said, "I didn't know that. I can hardly wait to go home to be the different kind of daughter and caregiver I want to be."

Rod Masumoto attended a session saying, "I don't write." At the end, he not only wrote a poem but he wept as he read his last line, "I don't want to feel." A few months later he showed me a notebook filled with thirty poems. His poems began by lashing out at God, then at life, then at himself as a beast. His writing, and his feelings, evolved and later poems spoke of love, dignity and compassion toward his mother and himself. Compare his poems "What Do I Feel?" (page 117), written at that session, and his untitled poem (page 117), written on the day of his mother's death. Over coffee one day, he confessed that he had been thinking of killing his mother and himself before he started writing. His writing became a tool to help him make sense of his experiences and provided a time to explore his emotions, which had been so overwhelming. "Do you know what I learned to do?" he told me. "I learned to put these feelings aside while I cared for my mother. These feelings can get in the way if I let them surface too much. I worked on them in writing in the wee hours of the morning." Writing let him discover his capacity to feel, and that made him the caregiver his mother needed.

My writing groups met once a month to share our stories and writings. It was a place for tears, silence, laughter and a place to know we were not alone. Mary Swisher describes one of these sessions in "A Daughter's Lament" (page 108). Similar responses occur at conferences and lectures when I deliver lines that speak the chilling truth, as in the previously mentioned "Oscar Time." There are also those who come up to me later saying, "I thought I was the only one who felt this way." Others thank me for discussing family issues so openly. One caregiver recently wrote, "You helped me so much, I felt like helping others, too, so I'm now volunteering at a health center."

But I don't know what to write about, you say. Here are a few tips:

1. **Go for that one blade of grass.** Don't think of the whole forest or the whole ball field or everything that happened yesterday. Just that one blade of grass. Think of one feel-

ing you're experiencing right now, one thought you're having, one event that happened. What are you looking at right now? (Not this book!) Where are you standing, what are you hearing? Write about that. My poem, "A Red Umbrella" (page 176) is an example of taking a single element and going from there.

It can be overwhelming if you try to think of the whole experience of caregiving. Your last complaint, success, hug with your loved one, exasperation with some professional or moment of "Aha!" will get you started. Let one word follow another.

2. **Don't worry about spelling, grammar or punctuation marks.** Just write down what you're feeling or think ing. It can be a phrase, a diary entry, a note to yourself, a fragment. To get started, whatever comes first will be fine. Here's an exercise to try: Write your own version of my poem "The Uncaring Caregiver" (see page 156), making a list of all the things you "don't care about" and stick that to your refrigerator or mirror.

3. **Feel free to write in any form that you like**. Poems, stories, or just fragments like a shopping list are all good. Whatever makes you comfortable, whatever comes to mind…just get your words down on paper. A journal entry can become a poem, as with my "A Red Umbrella," if you decide you want to explore a moment further.

Caregivers in my support groups often tell me that they hear my voice saying, "Write. Write…use this moment to be creative. Don't feel sorry for yourself." And so they write. ✺

Poems by Frances this morning
Reveal the feeling of the divine
In caregiving.

Can I?

SETSUKO YOSHIDA

How can this be?
Can I, too, reach this point
In caring for my eighty-four-year-old
husband
Who is returning to childlike ways?

Anger, resentment and frustrations
Overwhelm me at unexpected moments
Throughout the days and nights.

How can I deal with such feelings and thoughts?
Can poetry and journal writing bring me some solace?
To truly see me for who I am? ༄

Sensei (Teacher)

LINDA NAGATA

She came, notebook and pen in
hand,
To lead me out of my morose state,
Encouraging, cajoling, insisting
Write, write, write.

Others spoke of current dilemmas, emotions.
I was stuck in the past—a dozen years gone by
"Why am I so emotionally delayed?" my mind asked.

Then the wiser voice said, learn and move on.
Sensei says write, write, write,
Write about one small thing
I try to focus on one small thing
Dredging up the aged memories
Like buried garbage they are not pleasant,
Helplessness, anger, resentment.

Write, write, write
A miracle happens
The bitter emotions, softened, turn
Into acceptance and peace.
Write, write, write. ༈

The Group

Bob Oyafuso

I entered the Lemon Tree from
the parking lot and
guessed that the door to the right
would take me to the
group. I recognized Frances at the head of the table
and knew this was the group.

It took me a year to muster the courage to join the group
A year of self-doubts, what do I know about writing poetry
But the pains of caregiving was unyielding and relentless
I knew there was no other way.

I knew Frances from her blog and books and felt
A kinship despite having never met her.

I looked around and saw the faces of wisdom,
time, compassion and hope

I looked for men to share stories and quench
My lonely journey, but there were none.
No matter, women are better listeners
And they are smarter than men

I sat down and soon began telling my story of despair
Of the anger, resentment and hopelessness
I saw knowing faces and knew
I would no longer cry alone. ✵

Ode to Frances

BOB OYAFUSO

Giving comfort day or night

Is this my life?
Serving my wife's every need
Finding words to soothe her
anger

Crying when I could not quench her pain
Praying when all else failed
No one to assuage my hurt
or connect to my soul

Lost, lonely and depleted
My plight has no end
Enter *Breaking the Silence*°
an epiphany lifting my soul
finding meaning in caregiving

Understanding my shame
for prayers to relieve me
from my burden

Letting go of my anger,
for promises not kept.

Knowing the stings of resentment
and the silence of family.

Melting away the grief
from my harden heart

Thank you, Frances
I am found ॐ

°*One of Frances' books on caregiving*

A Daughter's Lament
(the labor of becoming our own mother)
MARY SWISHER

It's as if the overcast day has
Blown this unknown
Niobe of tears
Into our midst.

Silently she rains down her
Salty drops until it puddles at her youthful feet.
The first daughter tells her sorrow…"I left my mother
In 'that' home, my sister hates me, it breaks my heart."
Our Niobe gives an audible sob and we can feel her
Tears lap at our ankles.

The second daughter speaks. "My husband can no longer drive
He could get lost…and he knows it."

More tears, enough to put a monsoon to shame, and yet…

Another daughter has gone to work, left her mother-child
At day care.

The deluge continue, tissues mound into a white mountain now
We are sitting in a sacred lake

Another daughter: "My brilliant husband can't walk…on the floor
I can't…too heavy and my mom needs more and there's no money…"
She reads a poem, crying, out of breath.
By now we have become a Greek chorus
Buoyed on salty swells of tears

Our new daughter speaks
Amid gasping sobs, she cries, a desperate howl
For the mother she has lost, but still holds,
And will not let go. ✄

We are the moonbeams.
The caregivers who support each other.
We are the circle of wounded spirits

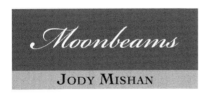

That come together to sing our hearts out.
We take back the night and bloom
together in the dark.

We are flowers of the night, sweet and true.

Through writing and sharing
We reawaken the sleeping spirit
And celebrate our beauty. ✄

Anger, resentment and frustrations
Explode like an erupting volcano.

Knowing that dementia has robbed my husband
Of his keen memory, his thinking capacity,
Does not help.

Reality

SETSUKO YOSHIDA

Caring for him day after day,
Love, compassion and understanding
Disappear into thin air.
Sitting quietly,
Facing the Buddha altar,
I meditate on my Reality.

My human frailties and limitations
Allow Unhindered Light and Eternal Life
To constantly illuminate and affirm my total being.

With palms together,
I bow in gratitude. ⁕

Dear God, if you must take Fran
please take her sooner rather than later.

Spare her the pains

A Prayer

BOB OYAFUSO

of an arthritic spine
the fear of lost words
the loneliness of bygone days
the anguish of home away.

I can't stand
    the non-conversations
    re-washing dishes
    searching for lost items
    removing trash from the freezer.

I am tired of
    cleaning her poop
    giving her medication
    keeping her from falling
    watching her sleep.

Please take her home.
Amen ✣

And now for Best Supporting Actress. Me:

for pretending blood in her toilet bowl
doesn't freeze me over.

Oscar Time

FRANCES KAKUGAWA

for being calm with an internal timepiece
that counts to ten when she is found on
the floor after a misstep.

for pretending her hallucinations of seeing an infant
in bed with her don't scare me half to death.

for nonchalantly cleaning her buttocks, her bedding,
her floor after a bathroom accident.

for wakening her cheerfully every morn with my singsong,
"Good morning, time for breakfast,"
while my body is still lying in bed elsewhere.

for quietly removing a painting from her bedroom
wall after her "Something black is coming out of that to get me."

for responding to her question as though it is being asked for the
first time instead of a hundred and fifty times.

for sitting in doctor's and emergency room's lounges
as though it is the chosen place to be, answering to
"Where am I?" every ten seconds.

for never raising my voice although another voice
is screaming inside.

and for saying, "I'm sure you'll live to be 100"
instead of "Dear God, when is this going to end?" ❧

Unspoken Mornings

FRANCES KAKUGAWA

Will lightning strike me
down
Before my first thoughts
find life?

How many mornings have I slipped
Groggily into her room, standing, watching,
A mother over a crib.
Her body curled in fetal position,
Her face toward the wall.
Still as curtains on a windless day.
"Is she breathing? Is she alive?
Is she finally gone, freeing me once again?"
I continue my sentinel watch.
"Yes, there is a light stir
Under her sheet."
During that split second
When morning was all stillness
A sense of relief washed over me
Like cool ocean waves on hot summer days,
Then shameless disappointment
When morning stirred
Into another day. ❧

Anger, it's your turn.

The others have spoken,

Some more eloquently than others,

Compassion, sadness, regret, even guilt.

The Boiling Pot

FRANCES KAKUGAWA

Today, the podium is yours.

Anger.

A wooden puzzle designed for preschoolers

Is placed in front of my ninety-year-old mother.

In a singsong voice, appropriate for a toddler,

The program director instructs my mother

To fit the puzzle pieces

Into each empty space.

If only the insertion of the banana

Into the right hollowed-out shape

Could recreate, replenish, impregnate

Cells plagued and tangled in her brain.

I want to scream at their loving efforts

To help stimulate my mother's dying brain

Back to life. I want to snatch the pieces

From my mother's hands and hurl them

Against the wall,

I want to shout, "Stop it! Stop it!"

But I know they can't.

No one can. ✤

Soon after she was diagnosed,
She began to fill a composition notebook
With her signature.

Five Notebooks

FRANCES KAKUGAWA

"So shame", she said," if I can't sign my name
nicely at the bank."

It became her favorite pastime:
Matsue Kakugawa, carefully written
Page after page after page.

As her disease progressed, Matsue Kakugawa
Began to lose a letter or two, and soon,
She was reduced to scribbles and lines.

Five notebooks, one-hundred sheets,
Two-hundred pages, twenty-two lines per page.
Twenty-two-thousand Matsue Kakugawas.

Twenty-two-thousand attempts
To save herself from the thief
Who was stealing her name. ✄

Caregiver Bio

· R O D   M A S U M O T O ·

Rod Masumoto worked as a safety specialist for the Honolulu Police Department while caring for his mother, Fusae Fujii Masumoto (1915–2012). Fusae had been a homemaker who later worked in the school cafeteria until she retired to care for her husband, who passed away in 1981. She was a talented baker who made an excellent apple pie—but her "ultimate dish" was her prune cake. No one could bake it as she did, even using her recipe. She also had a special gift: "My mother had this talent of being able to find things," Rod recalls. "When I was a kid, she was always there to find the right tools for me as I worked on model airplanes. All I had to ask was, 'Can you find...?' She did this when I was an adult, too, handing me whatever tools I needed while I did home renovations. It was sad to see her lose this ability." Rod was his mother's sole caregiver until she required 24-hour care. Now he has redirected his caregiving energy into remodeling his house and remaining readily available to help other caregivers. Today, Rod makes it a point to greet people when he's out, something he learned from Fusae, who loved all people. He calls this his "pay it forward" from his mom.

What do I see?
Do you see what I feel?
I feel more than you can ever see.
It hurts to feel.

What Do I Feel?

ROD MASUMOTO

I feel too, too much.
Minutes become hours,
Hours become days,
Days become years,

Years become a lifetime!
So sad to see,
So sad to feel.
I wish to feel nothing! ❧

In your hour of need,
I have learned to become a man.
A life to be a man,

Untitled

ROD MASUMOTO

A man who can feel the beauty
and warmth
Of a mother's love.
I will always feel your love,

Mom.
I wish to feel everything! ❧

Tug-of-War

Yes, yes, yes.
No, no, no.
Yes! No! Yes! No!
The pulling and tugging
Leaves nothing
But bruised palms, sweaty skin,
Pure exhaustion
For a game without winners.

The lure is constant
Between caregiver and patient.
The war cannot begin
Unless both ends are held,
One against the other.

Yes, yes, yes,
Yes, yes, yes.
The world held at one end,
No longer exists in the other.
This tug-of-war
Will not bring one into the other
For as long as one end
Is not held for the tugging,
The war cannot begin.

Just as there are two people in the caregiving relationship, there are two normal worlds—that of the caregiver's and that of the one being cared for. What we each perceive is both real and normal in the world we stand in. In their world, each time a question is repeated, they are asking it for the first time. Each time hallucinations occur, they are as real to them as our own realities are to us. When we

Two Normal Worlds

· C H A P T E R   F I V E ·

take our reason and rational thinking into their world, we create conflict. However, when we accept their world as being as real to them as ours is to us, caregiving takes on a different path with fewer conflicts.

Once I acknowledged that my mother's world was as normal to her as mine was to me, I dignified both of us with understanding and compassion, and eliminated unnecessary stress and negativism. I stopped denying, and instead embraced, the new person who was evolving right before my eyes. When my mother saw a "black thing" coming out of a painting on her bedroom wall, I quickly put it away saying, "I'll take it away so you won't see the black thing." I dignified her world by not denying what she saw. I had to believe there was a window to her mind that opened now and then, allowing her to know the world in which she had been reduced to live in had become strange and scary. To remind her of this would have been cruel and dehumanizing.

A loved one says, "John came to see me today." In your world, John has been dead for over ten years. Asking, "Did you have a good visit?" will continue the flow of communication and if you're lucky, she may share their conversation. To argue and tell her, "John is dead, Mom. You must have had a dream," drops a jagged rock in the middle of that stream that was flowing so smoothly until you arrived. Often, problems are caused by caregivers. Compare Elaine Okazaki's confrontation and frustration with her mother in "The Girl Did It" (page 123) to her acceptance of her mother's world, an acceptance which enables her to smoothly go back to bed, in "Humph, I Say" (page 124).

I write a monthly caregiving advice column for *The Hawai'i Herald*, a Japanese-American journal in Honolulu. One reader wrote in saying, "My wife hallucinates that there's always someone in the bathroom with her when I'm giving her a bath. She said she doesn't want to be naked in front of other people. This is a constant argument during bath time." I advised him, "Open the door of the bathroom and speak to her hallucinations and ask them to leave. Tell them your wife wants privacy, so *Leave!* Use body language and lead them out of the room. Ask your wife, 'Did I get everyone out?' Then close the door." Why argue? Who does it hurt when you tell people you don't see to go away?

Here is another example: A minister told me this story. When he visited his father in Japan, he found him cowering in bed, saying the room was filled with *tanuki* (badger dogs). So the son rolled up some newspaper and went around the room, chasing the imaginary tanuki out of the room. The room was filled with them, so he leapt around and hit the walls and talked to the tanuki, telling them to leave the room. Finally, his father said in Japanese, "Good, good, they're all gone now." And then son and father had a good visit. If the son had refused to enter his father's world, they would not have been able to enjoy their time together.

But what of our world? Are our loved ones incapable of entering our world? At certain stages of the disease, they will not be able to, not with logic and reason, but there is a place in our world that offers them a front row seat: dining in restaurants or around family gatherings, feeling the wind on their faces, hearing happy voices of family, feeling love and affection through human touch, being connected through conversations, even if they eventually are reduced to monologues. Our world offers the humanity of what it means to be human. It is understandable why we so want them in our world, to prove that they are still functional and well. This disease will not allow us this, not yet.

Enjoy both worlds for we are all as normal as normal can be.

Somewhere, in the unknown depths
Of her Alzheimer's soul,
Where even geniuses can't see,
There is light.

The Lie

FRANCES KAKUGAWA

Why then, would she,
Who has quietly eaten her lunch
Without a word and is dozing
In her own private room,
Suddenly look at me and ask,
"Is there enough food for everyone?
Shouldn't we be doing something?
Why are you the only one here?
Shouldn't we be calling everyone?"

Somewhere, in the obvious surface
Of her daughter's mind,
There is a license
To lie.

"Everyone was here," I gently explain.
"Everyone was happy.
You just had a big lunch."

"*Yokatta, Yokatta,*" she says.
"That's good. That's good.

I'm satisfied now.
I'm glad everyone came."
Somewhere, in the mysterious labyrinth

Of her mind,
She knows today is Christmas,
A time for family and food.

We are both comforted
By my lie. ❧

The Girl Did It!

ELAINE OKAZAKI

"The girl did it!
She made the shi-shi and the
doo-doo."
My mom utters in a tone of
admonishment.

"What girl? Where is she?
What are you talking about?" I question.
"Well, I didn't do this, you spiteful you," she answers.
"Who is this girl?" I ask again,
My frustration and impatience wide open.
"Well, if you don't know, I'm not telling you!"

I pull off the sheets and pillowcase and take them
To the laundry room along with her flannel nightgown,
Undergarments and other clothing.

How can she refer to the girl when she observes
Me during the process of cleaning up?
The washer is set, the cycle is complete,

I go to empty its contents only to discover
That the plastic-lined sheeting under her sheets
Are shredded, the cotton batting dissolved
Into very fine threads of yuck.
Such lint you never saw!

I sit down for a few moments to shed some tears.
Then a deep breath…
What else can go wrong? The start of another new day…
Wash…re-wash…wash again…dry…re-dry…

I'd like to find the girl who did it! ༈

I stand at the sink washing the morning dishes
When suddenly I feel a slight whizz on the side of my neck,

Humph, I Say

ELAINE OKAZAKI

From five yards away, the aim is
perfect from my mother.
This was the daily pill as pre-
scribed by her doctor
To curb her feisty behavior.
She has been declared legally blind by her ophthalmologist!
Humph, I say.

Then there's the protective wear for incontinence.
How often she's refused its usage, a barrage of denials,
No matter how many times I explain its need.

Found her soiled underclothing in the recesses of her closet
Or placed between articles of clothing in her dresser drawers.
She accuses me of entering her privacy.
Her internist says there's nothing wrong.
Humph, I respond.

Then there's the night she woke up screaming.
She shouted about that girl and that man in bed with her.
"Where's the man?" I stammer.
"Next to me, Can't you see?"
"And where's the girl?"
"Can't you see? Against the wall!"
"Well," I say, "Let the man sleep against the wall.
And put the girl next to you."
"Oh, okay," she utters.
Back to bed I go.
Humph! Humph!

She tells me her false teeth are missing; she can't find them.
We conduct a search of bathroom and bedroom,
Closets and drawers; look above, under and in between
After an hour or so, exhausted and spent
I lay on the floor and, staring at me from under the dresser
Is her plastic bag of curlers with her teeth.
Are they smiling?
Humph, I cry! ♂

Isobel sits in a rocker on the porch
talking quietly to birds on the lawn,
to people passing by, to creatures in the air
that neither you nor I can see. A world

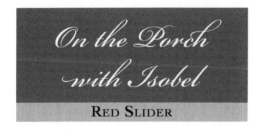

On the Porch
with Isobel

RED SLIDER

unto herself and, to me, a will in
the world
as fragile and trusting as it will
ever be.

She caresses the kitty-blanket on
her lap,
teases its fur between her thumb and finger,
the other hand brushing in wide circles
until it is completely known like a fine tool,
burnished with years of fond familiarity,
finger troughs worn deep on its grip.
Her head raises a little, her eyes open
and a brief smile crosses her face —
not her light-up-the-room smile with its
high wattage and disarming illumination.
Just the edges of smile, the contentment part
of suggestive gesture that signals more
a bit of there-ishness than here
as her hand bows a silent lullaby.

Keep still, it sings
so I can hear
the muish whisper
calling my thoughts to rest…

as if crossing the oceans to find herself
the meanings of "friend" call forth
the emptiness of an evening that falls
with the lightness of a purring cat.

I turn the pages…not reading
the nearly un-saying text
that sweeps the care from our minds;
sweeps our minds from the no-thought;
sweeps the bluish evening
into the textless night. ༝

Society

EUGENIE MITCHELL

When I was three or four
we had a sandbox in our yard
where I played
with my friend Jane.

I amused us both
by baking pretend pies
on my little kiddie stove.

When Mommy called me
to our real lunch
I always invited Jane.
Mommy set an extra place
and divvied up the carrot sticks
and sandwiches to share.
Jane was good, and polite — I saw to that,
passing along her every word of praise.

She even returned her uneaten food
so it wouldn't go to waste.
Mommy relished that —
as she cleared the dishes
from Jane's empty place.

So now when Mom summons "everyone"
to accompany us to the store,
or cajoles that "nice lady" in the mirror
to "come, come have fun" with her,
or worries that "all those people" I cannot see
haven't had enough to eat,
I mouth the-more-the-merrier,
not so much to humor Mom,
as to honor her,
for helping me to meet my need for society
when my brain was playing tricks on me
fifty years before. ✴

A Reflection

ELAINE OKAZAKI

She folded plastic bags into 2x2s
All creased meticulously, carefully stored
Between books, into handbags,
Stuffed into crevices, nooks, corners.

I ask her why.
"I can't remember," she utters.

She used rubber bands of all colors,
From the *Advertiser, Star-Bulletin*, to carefully

Band sets of five envelopes,
Found in every room of her tiny home.
Some rubber bands, placed on counters and shelves,
"To keep the ants away," she says.
I ask her why.
"I don't remember," she says.

Then there was the money,
Crisp greens of ones, fives, tens and even twenties
Found between pages, between books,
Inside articles of clothing, in dresser drawers.
I ask her why.
"How do I know?" she retorts angrily.

But the worst, fifteen cylindrical containers of Quaker oatmeal
All purchased on sale from Longs Drugs or Foodland market,
Found in one bedroom all on the floor.
On each lid, little worm-like creatures crawled freely!
"Why so many?" I ask.
She laughs.

Then there are the days she spent
Rummaging through her dresser drawers.
"What are you looking for?" I ask.
She answers angrily,
"I'm looking for…I'm looking for…
I'm looking for something!
Go away!" she answers angrily. ❧

Misdiagnosis

Another misdiagnosis: Hey Doc,
She ain't got no language/perception
Decay, she's merely turning into a poet,
A literary jewel of metaphors,
A perceiver of images unseen
By passersby, medical tests and research.
Ah, Doc,
Blessed are the poets
Born daily into our lives.

We often believe conversation is possible only through conventional spoken language. But an Alzheimer's patient doesn't hear the question the way we do, doesn't frame the answer how we would like it. We may find humor and meaning, instead of fear and helplessness, if we learn to hear through their ears. In fact, if we approach it from their side, we may find ourselves wondering, "Who's having the communication problem?"

Conversations

CAN WE TALK?

· C H A P T E R   S I X ·

Some of what our loved ones say may be nonsensical, refer to another time or place, or possibly invented whole cloth out of something they have perceived and interpreted in a way that doesn't match our reality. But it is important to listen because sometimes what may seem like outrageous accusations, such as theft or abuse, have a basis in reality. Remain calm, don't get frustrated, enter their world and ask questions that will help you discern the truth.

Conversation with an Alzheimer's patient can also sometimes be one-sided, but as difficult as it may be, it's important for us to remember to include our loved ones in our daily life. Thinking that communication requires spoken word deprives us of some of life's most treasured lessons. Our loved ones can speak volumes with their eyes and body language. In my children's book, *Wordsworth Dances the Waltz*, young Wordsworth's parents tell him, "If Grandma goes to Grandparents Day, she won't understand what's going on, so it's best to keep her home." How can we know what Grandma understands? Isolation will not improve our ability to converse with our loved ones.

It is also important that our conversations with our loved ones are carried on with dignity and respect. They are adults, not children. I was told at the time of my mother's diagnosis, that my mother was at the third grade level and would eventually regress to infancy. No…thinking of our loves ones as children would result in having us speak to them as children, demeaning and disrespecting who they still are. Even in her dementia, my mother could recognize when she was being patronized by insincere and condescending words. (See my poem, "Plastic Orchids," on page 158 and the discussion in that chapter on cultural beliefs and respect.)

The language we use when we talk about caregiving can create attitudes that change our behavior and perception of relationships with our loved ones. Take the word "coping." *I am coping with caregiving.* Replace "coping" with "embracing." *I am embracing caregiving.* Note how one word can change one's perception of how we view and live the life of a caregiver. If we hold on with grief to the person who is slowly disappearing, all that effort would not leave us with time and energy to acknowledge the new evolution of our loved one.

Another example is the word "defensive." Once we define a patient's behavior as defensive, that one word, "defensive," can create a particular attitude with feelings of hostility and anger. That goes on to affect our perceptions and behavior toward our loved one. Often, the simple use of language becomes the most powerful tool of preserving dignity.

When we speak to our loved ones, our choice of words can determine their responsive behavior. Take these phrases: "I told you," "How many times must I tell you?" They remind our loved ones that something is very wrong with them. They know this and there is no need for constant reminders. Toward the end, they may stop speaking to avoid being told, "I told you." I once heard a caregiver tell her husband, "Oh you remembered, very good." The underlying message was, "You have been forgetting a lot, but good for you, you remembered today." She thought she was being positive, but her message was one of belittlement—a message that he has been forgetting a lot. Why not a simple "Thank you" to dignify that moment?

Finally, I must address how doctors and the medical community communicate with us. My journal entry "I Am Not Old!" (page 146) and the accompanying poem, "On Becoming 69" (page 147) show the failure of one medical professional who saw me only as a birth date found on my chart.

Physicians, do you know the crucial role you play in our lives? You bring us so much comfort and confidence by the mere fact that we can always "call the doctor." You are that rare someone who's there for us, even in the wee hours of the night. Your phone number is always in our pocket. Nurses and all other medical personnel, we look to you, too, as we do to our physicians, for solutions and active and immediate references. We, too, often, are given additional responsibilities as caregivers. When caregivers discuss kindness and care found in medical offices, they are shared with joy and even tears of gratitude. We know science is not ready to deliver medical cures for Alzheimer's yet, but we do need your support on a human level. How about adding poetry to your medical school curriculum? ❧

Her words emerged haltingly,
her grimace showing strains
of forcing each word out.

Constipation

BOB OYAFUSO

She wants to tell me something important
I can't get the words out, she cries
the tears flow, I fold her in my arms
we both cry. ৵

Babbling…
sounds without words
a soliloquy on stage

Babblelese

FRANCES KAKUGAWA

her eyes on fire
her head nodding with passion
periods commas disappear her babbling
Continues chuckles laughter…

We speak our French, Italian,
English and even Japanese,
but no one, no one
has taught us Babblelese.
Why so much laughter in Babblelese?
Are all her secrets being released
Riding the winds on whose wings they fly?
Babblelese—
Language reserved
For the precious few. ৵

For one and a half years
She watched me quietly
As I visited my mother.
At age 102, she had no visitors.

Dear Mrs. Kono

FRANCES KAKUGAWA

She spoke not a word
But her eyes, so clear
Observed everyone in her midst.
She'd extend her hand for a shake
Or nod to me at my greeting.
But she somehow knew,
I was there for my mother.
Today, I visited her floor.
She took my hand
And held it tightly
And wouldn't let go.
"Do you remember me?"
I asked in Japanese.
She nodded, nodded, nodded nonstop,
Her fingers curled tightly into mine
As if a lifeline ran between us both.
Her eyes filled with tears
When I kissed the top of her head.
And still she clenched on.

Somehow she seems to know.
My mother is no longer here.
Somehow she seems to know,
I now have time and space
To love her as my own. ♨

Pull up your pants.

I don't have any pants.

These are your pants.

Can This Daughter Be Trusted?

EUGENIE MITCHELL

Aren't I a girl?

Yes. Girls can wear pants.

These pants are too tough.

Tight. I'll help you.

Don't knock me off.

Sorry. I'm pulling up your pants.

I thought you were knocking me off.

No, I love you. I'm trying to help you.

You're killing me.

I'm pulling up your pants.

I thought I was going to die.

You're not going to die.

(Oops. Her eyes know the lie.) ❧

Witness the day, the table, the resolve
that pours itself into new containers,
as if I hadn't been on hand the day before
to make the same mistakes I'll make

RED SLIDER

arranging things again to start over
again and do it anew, the buttons
on her shirt,
the noodles on the floor, the
sopping wet

Depends I'd just finished changing. Scoot
out the door, then out the door again
and then, out the door until we get it right
or get there late or give it up again, along
with some before that might have been
paren'd and pinned between yesterday's
begins and ends. Then, once more,

"Who are those people in the other room?
Have my students come for their lessons?"
That's the TV, Mom, just the TV on.
Come take your pills, they're on the table.
"Oh, first I need to go see who's here,
I hear them talking in the other room."

It's the TV, Mom, just the TV. Take your pills,
I'm poaching eggs for you. The water's
on the table, there. "I will. But first
I must see who is in the other room,

I can hear them speaking, don't you
hear them speaking? I do. I must
go and see. They may need me, don't
you think they do? Don't you hear them too?"

"Hello, this is Erik's TV Repair at 4th and Pine.
Do you know Isobel? She's here in my shop
but I don't think she knows quite where she is
or where she's been; just wandered in alone
and doesn't seem to know her way back home.
I asked if I could help, but she pointed to a TV
and said the people there had come in first
and she would wait her turn. No, not at all,
I offered her a chair, she's just sitting there
and talking to herself. I think she whispers
answers to the quiz show guests on the Sony
I just fixed. Yes, I thought it best she doesn't
wander off alone. Fine, I'll let her know
you're on the way. I'm here till six, Not at all,
glad to help, my mother's just about her age."

3 a.m. or 4 a.m., it doesn't matter on this watch.
Whatever follows is whatever follows next —
detached from all routines and regularity,
my schedule tunes to sudden expectations —
Isobel's in bed asleep, the TV's off and I am too,
my face is resting on a smear of sticky jelly
on the table; my mind a blur of kitchen LEDs,

though I hear the visitors that come and go
at her request. Is she in bed? The dialogues
with students that blend sounds that burst
in sentences and then impromptu verse.
Did I wipe up the jelly? Is she in bed?
Are those quiz shows whizzing by?
Did I pick her up from Erik's shop?
Is the TV off? Is that jelly on the table?

Are we late again, are we really out the door?
Is the TV off? Is that jelly on my cheek?
Is she actually asleep? Is the TV off? ৶

Shhhhh

From *Wordsworth Dances the Waltz*

FRANCES KAKUGAWA

Hush, hush,
Grandma's losing her memory.
Hush, hush,
She's forgetting

To flush the john.
Hush, hush,
She's lost her glasses again.
Hush, hush,
She's forgotten my name. •
Hush, hush,
Shhhhh. ৶

Caregiver Bio

·LINDA DONAHUE·

Linda Donahue lives with her husband, Michael, and sister, Barbara, in Elk Grove, California. All three became caregivers for Linda and Barbara's mother, Rhea Read (1922–2014), during Rhea's struggle with Alzheimer's and its complications. In addition to raising three daughters, Rhea was an active choir member with a beautiful alto voice, a church secretary and a hospital volunteer whose radiant smile touched many lives. Although caregiving was Linda's most demanding and rewarding occupation, she has also been an English and German language teacher, birdwatcher, medical transcriber, dropout, janitor, pianist, computer programmer, china trader, pottery collector and cat rescuer. Serendipity led her to Frances Kakugawa's Writing for Caregivers support group in Sacramento, and she is ever grateful to Frances for her inspiration and encouragement. In poetry, Linda found the means to bear witness to her mother's difficult journey and express her own feelings of sorrow, helplessness, gratitude, love and loss.

Crossword puzzles, Scrabble games,
Latin phrases, archaic terms
from classic English literature,
any word she'd never heard before:

so many reasons
to pick up a dictionary,
and she did, nearly every day.
Until recently.

Her library of vocabulary
acquired over a lifetime
atrophies in the stacks,
inaccessible behind
misfiring synapses.
Meaning, spelling,
pronunciation disconnect
as the cross-referencing system
disintegrates.

Her speech becomes
tentative and halting.
She turns words over
like cards laid face down
for a game of Go Fish,
hoping to find a match.
When she can't,
she lapses into silence.
So we sit saying nothing

in a place beyond speech,
unburdened of the need for
nouns and verbs.

She communicates best
in body talk now: physical stance,
hand motions, vocal tone,
muscle tension and expression
are the basic linguistic
elements.

Sometimes she smiles
as if in secret pleasure
at the inexpressible.
Do her relaxed facial
muscles speak?
Do they tell me
she's relinquished,
for now, the taxing struggle
for words?
Do they say
Watch me as I slip
into a moment of unspeakable
freedom and
peace? ❧

This morning
you did not pretend to read the paper.
I read the front page
holding back tears,

Getting Lost
MARY SWISHER

afraid to start
a conversation you might get
lost in, like some brambly
blackberry mound.

I clear my throat and say
"Afghanistan, this is about Afghanistan."
You come as from a dream
and say, "Your eyes are so mysterious this morning."
How can I not love you for this
mischievous change of subject?

You look deep in my eyes…your brown eyes unguarded
like an innocent child.
"Mysterious," I say, "In what way?"
"Too-ra-loo-ra-loo-ra," you sing back,
and I have become lost in your world,
a bramble of enchanted
connections for me to untangle. ✄

One thought keeps running through my head
As I sit here holding your hand.
You no longer know my face,
I'm but a stranger who comes to you

As you sit in total silence
Day after day after day.
Whatever thoughts there seem
to be
Lay buried deep inside of you.

Your brain no longer sends messages
To your colon, to your bladder,
Not even a light whisper.
Your legs no longer know how to walk
Or even crawl. And what I thought
Was so innate with birth, swallowing and chewing
Have disappeared.

Perhaps you are ready to go.
The men in white say you are already gone.
But your heart continues to beat
Deep inside of you where even they cannot see.
Your eyes conceal wherever that you are.
My own limitations do not allow me entry
Inside of you where you exist.

So I sit here holding on tight, for if you go,
I will no longer be Somebody's Child. ❧

The young doctor, and why do they all look so young these days, looked at my birth date before asking me why I was there.

"Oh," she said, "You don't look your age."

I Am Not Old!

FRANCES KAKUGAWA

After I told her the details of all the pain I was experiencing, she said, "Seems like you still have a few good years left, so I'll give you this prescription." A prescription without even touching her stethoscope to my heart? A prescription without even knowing the cause of my pain? Do young doctors know magic?

To my "What will this prescription do?" she responded, "It'll stop your brain from sending pain to your body."

"No," I said, "I can stand this pain. I need to know the cause of this pain before getting a prescription." She insisted on the prescription, so I took it and left it in the trash can on my way out. Besides, my ten-minute office visit was up.

Aside from feeling angry and insulted (Don't medical schools teach students that calling a woman old is worse than bird flu?), I felt very sad that these young doctors see the elderly as people who don't deserve medical diagnosis.

I didn't have the time nor interest to tell her I have more than a few good years left, working with the elderly and sick, with respect, love, compassion and dignity, and of the incredible life lessons we continue to learn from each of them. I didn't tell her this. She didn't hear me when I told her I had pain; why would she hear me now? ✣

How can I be sixty-nine when I feel forty-nine?
How can my mother's daughter turn sixty-nine?
For God's sake, children aren't supposed to age.
Not children born out of mothers' wombs.

On Becoming 69

FRANCES KAKUGAWA

This poem speaks to those who see the elderly as having lived out their lives after age sixty-five and who believe that only productivity in the workplace has human worth. Yes, Dylan Thomas, I am once again raging against the dying of the light.

How can my mother's daughter
turn sixty-nine?
Four years ago, it all began…
They called me elderly,
Neatly categorized under OLD.
They began mailing me funeral
plans,
Nursing home ads on slick col-
ored sheets
In large black print.
They gave me flu shots before
anyone else,
Invitations to free luncheons
By long-term care insurance agents.
"You are dying," their messages said.
Shall I tell them of my eighty-eigth birthday
When I plan to make love and hear the leaves move
On a windless day? ✨

When I am eighty-eight
I will have a love affair
That will leave me trembling
On a windless day.

When I Am 88

FRANCES KAKUGAWA

I will feel the brush strokes
Of Van Gogh,
Clawing, bleeding
My inner flesh.
I will be Shakespeare
Vibrant, on stage,
Rivers rushing, splashing
Over moss and stone.
I will become soft,
Sensuous, wet
Against your skin,
Silk against steel.
When I am eighty-eight
I will still be woman,
Yes! ✻

I will drown in Puccini,
Mozart, Verdi.
Tidal waves roaring
Inside of me.

Conversations: Can We Talk?

PO Box Hawai'i, USA

Excerpted from "The Scarf" (see page 159)

I am…gasping…for…breath
This box once spelled home
Suddenly closes in on me,
Constricting my breath.
My legs and arms entangled
In cultural webs of myths and lore
From ancestral lands,
Eulogized with social rules:
How I should live, Who I should be,
What is right, What brings shame.
One way or the other, freezes me into ice.
This self, created by years of containment
Fashioned for the public will
Now threatens to bust free.
I have become a truth that doesn't exist
Outside of this box. Oh life!
Contaminate me! Strip off my white robe,
My robe of air-tight alibis,
Formulas on how to be, a social perfection.
Oh, strip me good.
Wrap your blanket full of holes
With wildness of life, around my naked body,
Let me slush around in the sewers of your life
Right up to my open wounds to suck it dry.
Take me. Take me
Where freedom without judges
Is the ensign of my existence.
Now, Life! Before I am too dead.

There is a whole new culture in caregiving, one created by non-caregivers. It is cocoon-like, and once a person becomes a caregiver, isolation and alienation begin to occur. We are viewed as aliens from a world that offers only discomfort to others —

we are avoided by friends and non-caregiving family members. Caregivers are seen as being too busy to be part of the "normal" interactive world. We and our loved ones live with a disease that makes it difficult to visit and socialize. Doctors and health personnel often look to caregivers to provide what the medical world is unable to deliver — they cannot give us a cure, so we must serve to comfort and aid our loved ones as best we can. The caregiver's world becomes a culture of isolation, fear and endless responsibilities.

We also bring our own influences to the caregiving culture — a combination of our ethnic traditions and general social etiquette which can sometimes interfere with medical and caregiving needs. Some of this is attached to shame or fear: *What will others say or think? If I don't present a perfect public face, I'll be seen as an incompetent person. I must protect my loved one and not let anyone know she or he is ill. I must "save face" for the sake of the family.* Many of us have also been brought up to believe *I must be polite and refrain from imposing on others, even at the expense of draining myself of energy and health.*

Shame can prevent us from seizing a rare moment of joy with our loved ones. Take, for instance, Mary Swisher's poem, "Music and the Brain" (page 154). Would you have danced in the parking lot as she did? Or would embarrassment have kept you a "proper," controlled caregiver? With Alzheimer's in our lives, we need to re-evaluate what makes us feel ashamed. We

grow a thicker skin so that the stares of people who don't understand our world no longer bother us. Our idea of what is an
acceptable outfit for going outside changes. With everything a
caregiver has going on in his or her life, something has to give —
shame and embarrassment should be the first to go.

A traditional culture of self-effacement can keep us from seeking help when we most need it. "It took me a while to attend the
support group because, being Japanese, I didn't want anyone
to know. I thought, *If anyone hears I'm going to a support group, I'd
be embarrassed*," said Elaine Okazaki. "'Support group' connotes
weakness, needy. Once I came, I was so glad…it was a place to
go to on Saturdays. I felt such a void when [our group stopped
meeting]."

So while we need to put aside certain cultural beliefs because
they add unnecessary burden to caregivers, there is a need
to become aware of instances when culture needs to be honored. For example, in my poem "Plastic Orchids" (page 158),
my mother is called by her first name by a health worker who
professes her love. I applaud my mother's indignant response.
Every culture comes with specific language, behavior and prac-
tices to preserve honor and dignity, particularly between older
and younger individuals, or strangers. While a health worker's
culture may use terms of endearments freely, this familiarity
may be insulting to a person of another culture, or give cause for
confusion. To be called "Papa-san" when he was "Doctor" in his
pre-Alzheimer's days is not only demeaning to a distinguished
gentleman, but may elicit no response to this unknown term.

Certain cultures believe in not sending a person into the other
world on an empty stomach. This can interfere with a patient's
health directive which states there is to be no tube feeding.
A situation like this requires communication to balance the
required medical care with the cultural needs to keep the patient

and their family comfortable and happy. Open discussion and education are necessary to reduce the gaps between culture and medical science.

Ideally, we need to free ourselves from cultural teachings that create barriers to our well-being and preserve those that maintain honor and respect even during the last stages of life. ✻

They say when speech leaves us,
When the words tangle up
Refuse to come tripping on the tongue
That song or music makes sense.

Music & The Brain
MARY SWISHER

You still recite all the
bones of the hand
Rage against the politics
of the day

And I am here to say that you have turned into a human jukebox
Breaking into Cole Porter songs, memory perfect words.
Anywhere anytime, much to the amazement and delight of friends
You croon and invite all to dance.
Today in the farmers' market you stopped in your tracks
Amazed at the color of the vegetables and fruit
Fascinated with pavilions catching the north wind
Then broke into "Button up your overcoat when the wind is cold…"
And we danced to the car like Ginger and Fred. ⋆

A Yellow Plumeria
FRANCES KAKUGAWA

"Here, take your pick,"
he offers me.
I look into his Safeway
plastic shopping bag

And am greeted with fragrance from pink and yellow plumerias.
"Oh," I say, "Can I have a yellow one? I love yellow."
He smiles and says, "Yes, take your pick."

I take a yellow plumeria still wet with dew
And take it to my face to enjoy its fragrance.
He smiles as though he has given me gold.
I gingerly hold the blossom in one hand
As I continue down the aisle with my shopping cart
To find my ginkgo and cranberry capsules.

I turn to look at the man who in one simple instant
Seems to have said, "You are a beautiful woman,
You deserve a flower."

His shirt and oversized pants are wrinkled and caked
Like the rivers that run on his face and down his arms.
His hair, matted with the morning rain, sticks to his neck.
His rubber zoris do not protect his muddy feet.
Yet his eyes shine with pride as he goes from one stranger to the next,
Offering his flowers like Mother Earth each morn.

Soon I see salesclerks with flowers in their hair or behind their ears
And my heart overflows with love for all the strangers
Who have accepted his gift.

The fragrance fills my car as I drive home.
So much fragrance from one simple blossom.
Why am I filled with such joy when all around me
Plumeria trees are in abundance?
Why do I feel so beautiful from one little blossom
Given to me by one flower child,

All grown up in borrowed clothes?
Why do I feel poetic and special all day long?

In late evening I look at the flower, wilted in heat.
If he were my father or my brother,
Would I bless him for his gift
Or would I say, embarrassed, "Stop that. You can't do this.
Don't be a pest. Go home."
Why am I so tolerant toward strangers who give me flowers
But won't allow those close to me to do the same? ♨

The Uncaring Caregiver

FRANCES KAKUGAWA

I am that uncaring caregiver:
I don't care if I'm late for her
appointment
Or totally miss a calendar date.
I don't care if she doesn't eat
breakfast,
Or refuses a snack or two.
I don't care if we miss a bath time
Two days in a row.
She's not meeting the president
And if she is, I'm sure the president
Wouldn't know.

I don't care if she lets out a yell
In a restaurant filled with diners,
Chews her food without etiquette rules

And spills her water all over me.
I don't care.

I don't care if the flowers have died,
I don't care if the dust leaves fingerprints
On tabletops and furniture, and yesterday's
Dishes are in tomorrow's sink.
I don't care if the telephone's been cut off
And my paper pile grows by day and night
When we're both fast asleep.
I don't care.

I don't care if my jeans are on backward,
Or my shoes are of two different styles
On each swollen foot. And my grey roots
Are an inch long, my bangs over half my sight.
I don't care.

I'm a caregiver and I don't care
Of stuff that means nothing
When my mother's smiling and asking,
Are you Hideko?
That's when I care. ❧

"Matsue, I love you.
Matsue, I love you."
The aide sing-songs to my mother,
As she lifts her

Plastic Orchids

FRANCES KAKUGAWA

Out of her wheelchair.
"Bullshit," I hear my mother say.
"Bullshit," once again, quietly
To herself but I hear her

From the doorway of her room.
Yes, bullshit. In her generation
No one calls her Matsue except
Older siblings, her husband, parents.
Everyone else bestows respect with
"Matsue-san."
A stranger calling her Matsue
And vowing love
Is as genuine as a stem
Of plastic orchids.

"I have six months to live," she began over the phone, as though her story needed a climactic beginning. "Two weeks ago I was getting dressed to go to Mr. Mishan's funeral when I began having trouble breathing. I went to the ER. They found water in my lungs. The doctor decided to do more tests so I was kept in the hospital for a week. They found cancer in my ovaries. It's at level four which means it's very advanced."

The Scarf

FRANCES KAKUGAWA

"The Scarf" is about "Nora," a caregiver from my group. She was always there and when she called and said, "I'm dying," I took my pen and kept a journal from that moment on to her last breath. I never imagined that one of the caregivers from my circle would face death before her loved one. In "The Scarf" you will see how cultural upbringing and beliefs, personal values and relationships are all part of the blended experience of the caregiver.

She continued her story, pronouncing each word slowly and carefully. "The doctor said it's too advanced for surgery but I could have other treatments. I told him, 'If I have chemo, I know my hair will all fall out. I had a good and long life so I'm not taking any treatment.' He told me to go home and think about it, but I told him I don't need to think about it. I asked him, 'How long do I have?' and he said six months. He said he never had a patient like me before." *Oh, Nora, I am hearing, I am hearing each word being said.* Somewhat clumsily, I interjected with, "I'm so sorry, Nora, what can I do for you?" She graciously thanked me, assuring me she was ready to die.

"I feel blessed because now I am given time to clean up our house and get all my papers in order. I'm such a rubbish collector. I need to sort things out." She concluded this disturbing conversation with, "I started to knit a scarf for you, but I don't think I can finish it in time."

I'm tiptoeing, I'm tiptoeing. "Oh, thank you for thinking of me. Please don't worry about the scarf, save your energy for your health."

Four years ago Nora walked into my writing support group for caregivers at the Alzheimer's Association in Honolulu. She came into library quietly, without a word, nodded her head to me in greeting, put her handbag slowly on the floor, pulled out a chair from under the wooden table, reached down to take out a sheet of paper and pen from her handbag and sat down. All this was done without a sound, as though any movement or sound she caused would disrupt the room or she feared she was taking more than her allowance of space. She introduced herself and we all leaned our heads toward her to hear her softly spoken voice, "I can't write but I came just to listen because I heard Frances speak last month."

I recognized her from a writing workshop I had given to caregivers at Tripler Hospital. She was a tiny woman, less than four feet, ten inches tall, dressed in a light blue *mu'umu'u* with puffed sleeves. She articulated each word slowly as though each word was being processed through her mind before being spoken. *Be patient, be patient, she is teaching you patience...stop running, walk and listen.*

I turned into a broken record each time she shared a story, "Nora, write that down." Nora felt comfortable speaking in Japanese. Often, with encouragement, she wrote in both Japanese and English. Japanese captured what her English lost in translation.

She had been a caregiver for her father and then her parents-in-law. Now, she was caring for her elderly mother who was over 100 years old. "Last week the neighbors called the police at three o'clock in the morning because they heard me yelling at my mother." In elegant Japanese, she repeated what she had shouted to her mother. Her Japanese was formal, not vernacular, "Mother, I don't know what to do anymore because I am so tired. If you don't go to bed, I won't be able to sleep." *Oh, neighbors, if only you understood Japanese, you would have heard Nora use the honorific dialect which signals respect, love and honor. Oh, if only you knew her mother has a hearing problem and so raised voices must be employed.*

Nora was married to a World War II veteran who had been a prisoner in a German town until the end of the war. They were both second-generation Japanese-Americans. "My husband is the typical *samurai*. He doesn't tell me how he feels about things. He's happy as long as I cook and take care of him. But I want to travel — I want to take a cruise but he won't go. When he was a prisoner, he was kept in a house with a family. The family was very nice to him. Last week we got a letter from the daughter who was just a child when my husband was there. Her parents are now gone. I told my husband we should go to Germany and thank this family but he said, 'What for?' He won't talk about the war."

She was a product of parents who raised her according to strict Japanese cultural mores. Her father kept a daily journal in Japanese, which became his means of educating Nora. When I pushed Nora to write, she confessed, "I don't like to write because my father used to sit me down and read his journal to me. He did this when I did something improper or wrong. I just hated to sit and listen to him."

She was raised to believe a woman took care of her husband and children with gratitude. She shared, "My mother always told me to accept life as it is. All suffering is my fate for being a woman. On the day I got married, my mother told me: *'Sekai de ichiban hitori musume, kawaii watashi no hitori go Michiko. Takeshi-san to nakayoku tanoshiku, sugoshi nasai ne. Kodomo tachi kawaii gattai ne Okāsan inute iru yo.'* (In this whole wide universe, I have only one child, my adorable daughter called Michiko. Marry Takeshi and have a loving life with him. Be one with him in heart. I will be waiting to see adorable children someday.)"

Nora struggled with guilt, feeling she was dishonoring all that her parents taught her about filial piety when she placed her mother in a private nursing home. Encouraged to write a letter to her mother, she wrote in formal Japanese, "Forgive me, Mother, for being such an ungrateful daughter. I put you in this care home because I cannot take care of you anymore. I don't visit you every day. I didn't visit you on your birthday last week because it hurt me too much to see you as you are today. Please forgive me. I am such an ungrateful daughter."

Not long after her mother's death, Nora became a caregiver for her husband. "This is my lot in life. I was born to take care of others. I should be happy I can take care of him. If I think this way, I don't feel so bad."

And yet, the subject of a cruise came up again and again, it was her dream cruise. *Oh, Nora, I wish I could put wings on you and let you fly with freedom.* Subtly, subtly, I came in the back door with my poems written for her:

I am generations of women
Looking in at layers of silk *kimonos*,
Muffled giggles, *koto* movements,
Knowing they can only be

Mere images of desire.
I am generations of women
Waiting to be dragonfly wings,

A maple leaf, spiraling snowflake,
A cherry blossom,
Released and detached from
Generations of cultural clasps.

I am generations of women,
Suppressed in thin *yukata*
Stuck ankle deep in rice fields,
Scarecrows on wooden stakes.
Denied, yet desiring wantonness
Beneath layers of silk.
I am woman,
Suppressed,
Dying.

Nisei: second-generation Japanese-American
Yukata: cotton kimono

"I am Japanese and this is my lot," echoed over and over again.
I wrote this poem after taking a few lessons in Japanese flower
arrangement. "Here, Nora," I said, "Take off your kimono if it's
stifling you."

Lesson #1
From *sensei* (teacher):
"Conceal the front rim
of the vase

With fern or flowers.
The front is not seen
Just as a woman

Keeps the front of her kimono
Closed, by taking tiny steps."
      "Yes, Sensei."
      I bow to the sensei.
      I am obedient.

Lesson #2
"We do not worry about the back of the vase.
Ikebana is placed against the wall.
Only front matters."
      Hmmm…was I raised to be an ikebana?
      Always show saved face?
      Do not expose what is not seen?
This is being Japanese?
Yes, smile?
      Bow, be nice?
      Let no one know
      What weeps deep inside?
      Desires, needs, dreams?
      No, only front matters?
      Keep buried, like samurai swords
      And Japanese porcelain dolls
      After Pearl Harbor, Hiroshima?
      Yes, smile, be nice?
      Only front matters?

Lesson #3
"Ah, maybe put orange flower
In the back, behind yellow protea.

Good to see little color from back."

No! No more shadowing.

Let my voice entombed

For generations break the silence

Of the Buddhist hall.

I am not Ikebana.

I am not mere heaven, man and earth

Rooted by cultural hands.

Sift those sands. Yes!

I am free!

I am tossed into the winds.

I shed my kimono.

I spread my legs.

I am free.

A few months into our sessions, Nora began to arrive with a twinkle in her eye and a soft smile on her face, "I went to my first matinee movie by myself. Thank you for suggesting it, Frances. I heard your voice encouraging me."

"I went to a health conference at the hotel in Waikīkī. I stayed overnight and took a room and I felt good eating in a restaurant by myself. I asked my husband to join me but he didn't want to so I went by myself."

"Thank you for the McDonald's and Starbucks gift certificates. I took a bus to Starbucks after our session last month and had a cup of café mocha just as you suggested. It was so good. I enjoyed being there by myself. I didn't have to worry about anyone."

Slowly, slowly, I saw the loosening of the bonds that held her tightly. *Yes, take larger strides, it will take you there faster and sooner.*

Her husband began needing more care, her lifelong dream of going on a cruise began to dim. "My husband can't travel anymore because he's in a wheelchair and needs to be near a bathroom. Now, I'll never go on that cruise."

"Nora," I said, "Take a cruise by yourself. You can do that," and she said, "Yes, you're right, someday I will."

Nora had been married for almost fifty years. One night, after being in our support group for almost a year, she invited her husband to watch her take a shower. "I asked him if he wanted to see me take a shower and luckily his wheelchair fitted through the bathroom door so for the first time in our married life, he saw me naked. He seemed to have enjoyed it even if he didn't say anything."

Ah, Nora, don't you see, you are on a cruise right now. You are sailing with wings on your feet. Look at you now.

Nora continued to loosen her kimono. One morning she brought in an article on how music and learning new things improve the minds of the elderly. With encouragement and permission, Nora began piano lessons, fulfilling a secret desire from her youth. An aura developed around her, an aura of joy. Lessons led to her first recital. She walked at a faster pace, she spoke with fewer pauses and her voice vibrated with life. And the sparkle in her eyes could no longer be hidden behind her Japanese fan.
I smiled the day she called me to say, "I have a crush on my piano teacher. He's younger than me but I like him. He's so kind and helps me so much. I can't believe I feel all this for him. I feel like a young girl."

"Nora! There's hope for you. I'm so happy to hear this."
"You're not going to lecture me on how silly I am, that I'm an old lady and shouldn't have crushes like this?"

"Nora, isn't it a wonderful place to be, to feel such joy, such excitement? Some people go through life unable to feel so strongly. Count this as a blessing."

"Thank you for saying all this. I don't plan to do anything about these feelings, it's just good to have them. This is why I look forward to my lessons. I don't play that good but he's so kind to me."

Some months later she called. "I'm sort of depressed. My piano teacher is moving his studio to the other side of the island and referred me to another teacher. I don't think I'll continue my lessons."

"Nora," I consoled, after suggesting she see her physician for her depression, "It's okay to continue your feelings for your teacher. Just flow with it. I do wish you'd continue your lessons with the new teacher. You enjoy the music you play and who knows, Nora, your new teacher might turn into a bigger crush."

She laughed. "The new teacher is a woman."

A few weeks later her voice reclaimed the joy it seemed to have lost before. "I told my doctor what you said and he agreed with you. So I'm taking lessons from this woman. He gave me some medication for my depression. He also said I must continue this support group because it's good for me." She continued her lessons until caregiving took this leisure time away from her.

"Frances," she proudly told me one day, "I bought a computer and my husband and I are taking lessons. I decided I'm not too old to learn new things. Now I can email you after you move to Sacramento." And she did for two years.

Three weeks after being diagnosed with cancer, she moved into a private care home to be under the care of the hospice program.

"I don't want to die at home because some cultures don't like to buy houses where someone died in it and someday if my husband and sons want to sell this house, I want them to be able to sell it. So coming to this home is perfect. And Frances, I'm still trying to work on your scarf."

"Nora, send me the scarf even if you don't finish it. I want it because you're making it."

"But you'll choke on it if I don't finish it," she laughed. "It can hardly go around your neck right now."

"Oh, I can hang it on the wall like a piece of art. Or I can choke on it each time I use it."

On Christmas Day I asked her, "How are you feeling, Nora? Do you feel lonely at night when everyone's asleep? What do you think about before you fall asleep?"

"No, I don't feel lonely. I'm just looking forward to being with God. It's not that easy to die. I wear Depends now. I am so blessed. Elaine comes to visit me. I got a card from Jason and Linda. My husband still thinks I'm going home and is in denial. I asked him to come stay with me here but he said he'll feel more comfortable at home. My sons hug me and I feel so loved. Before I left home, my son saw your poetry books in the boxes and he asked if he could have them. I felt good he wanted your books. My mother died so peacefully and I thought it would be that way for me, too. It's not easy to die."

"Nora, you have taken care of all the details of your dying, maybe you need to spend the rest of your time on living instead of dying."

"Oh, what wisdom," she responded, gasping for breath. "Elaine visited me today and when she left I thought I may never see her again but I need to say, 'I will see Elaine again. Yes, I will.' Thank you."

"Nora, I'm going to Hawai'i in March to give a talk. I'm going to see you then."

"Before today, I would have said I'll be gone by then but today, I'm going to say, I will see you in March. That's only four months, so I will see you. I'll live until then."

"And Nora, remember that scarf? I want to wear that scarf. Finish it for me."

"I have seventeen more inches to knit and if I do one inch a day, maybe I can finish it in time."

Nora's firstborn son was killed at age three when a car hit him while he was riding his tricycle. Nora was giving birth to her second son in the hospital when the accident happened. To protect Nora from grief, a family decision was made to have burial services before she returned from the hospital with her newborn son. "I never got to see my son again."

Her youngest son has been missing for years somewhere on an island in the Pacific. Hired investigators have been unsuccessful in locating him. "I guess I'm going to die without seeing him. This makes me sad. I gave birth to four sons and I have only two now."

Her voice no longer sounded light and upbeat. She was placed on oxygen and her pain managed with morphine although she never mentioned her pain at all. "So many people want to help me but I've never received help like this before. I was the one taking care of others all of my life. It's hard for me to accept help."

"Nora, let others care for you now. When someone wants to do something for you, you need to let them do this because when you receive, they too, are receiving and you can't deny that gift to others. It's a two-way gift. When I send something to you, it's for me, too. It's my way of telling you I love you. And this is all I can do from here."

"Thank you. Yes, you are right. I won't stop friends and family who want to help me. It's my turn now."

Nora often spoke of wanting to be free as a bird. "When I'm stuck in traffic, I used to tell my husband, I wish I could be a bird so I can just fly over all the cars and be on time for my appointment. I told my husband to release colorful pigeons at the end of my funeral service but he said it's too much of a problem."

This is about Nora, not you!!! Get those pigeons!!!

I sent her a set of glass bird ornaments that move and sparkle in light. "Nora, I bought myself the same set of birds and every Christmas I'll be putting them on my tree and you will be here in memory. I'm telling you this because I want you to know what's going to happen after you're gone. You will not be forgotten."

She responded with silence followed by a soft "Thank you."
Ah, Nora, bless you for leaving all doors open, even one for my feeble attempt at being ha-ha funny.

"Nora, I expect you to come to greet me when it's my turn to die. And I expect a mink-covered recliner waiting for me. You've got to arrange that when you're in heaven. I'll try to live a good life till then." She managed to laugh despite her constant coughing.

"Frances, I guess I'm not going to take that dream cruise after all. I told the care home owner to bag all my clothes and send them home. I don't need much. And don't send me anything anymore."

"Nora, maybe you're taking the ultimate cruise which is the cruise to heaven."

"A cruise to heaven. I like that."

Our conversations grew brief. "Nora, I love you. You are a gift to me. Thank you."

"I love you, too, and thank you for being my friend. I'm so blessed. I'm so lucky."

I sent her the following poem to which she responded, "I don't deserve all these words."

you are that lotus blossom
rising above the murky waters

lifting its face toward
the morning sun.
you are that first crocus
seeking its way
out of the cold icy ground
the magic that is spring.
you are that sunflower
searching for light
in the midst of summer
for all its glory.
you are a raindrop
on desert plains

bringing magic, wonder
on arid soil.
you are the painted hills
fiery in all their brilliance
awaiting the first fall
of winter's splendor.
you are wings in flight
over freeways, cities,
mountains, bridges
and ships on sea.

you are all seasons,
vines into grapes
grapes into wine
journeying without end.
thank you, my friend
for the lessons taught,
lessons lived
of how it is to be born,
to live, to die and to live
once again in every season
for life eternal.

I sent manuscripts of my two children's books to our friend
Elaine to be read to Nora on a good visit. They were expected
to be published after her predicted six months were to run out.
Nora was at most of my book signings, poetry readings, and
workshops open to the public during the four years we knew
each other. I'd look out into the audience and there she'd be,
smiling, dressed in her colorful mu'umu'u and a flower in her

hair. No small accomplishment as Nora made her way to newly found freedom on crowded city buses. There were days when she walked in with an umbrella, her hair wet with raindrops.

I called Nora to wish her a happy new year. I found myself reciting the traditional formal Japanese greeting, bowing my head in respect. I left the second line of the greeting unsaid because for a split second, the thought of speaking of life in the new year didn't seem appropriate. When she whispered hello, I said, "Nora, this is Frances. *Akemashite omedetō gozaimasu.*" Through her labored breathing she slowly returned the following greeting in a formal recitative voice, pausing to catch her breath, reciting syllable by syllable, "*Akemashite omedetō gozaimasu. Konnen-mo yoroshiku onegai shimasu.*" ("Happy New Year. This year, once again, I ask for your kind indulgence.")

"Yes," I managed, moved that she completed the greeting asking me with deep humility, to continue our relationship in the newly awakened year.

Shifting her voice to more casual language, she added, "I thought I was going to die last night but I'm still here today. I'm going to work on your scarf when I'm feeling better. It's not turning out nice. I'm running out of yarn and I don't want to bother my son to get me more yarn."

Call Nora, I thought. I was rushing out to my doctor's appointment at 11:55 and thought, *I'll do it later, I'm running behind.*

Call Nora entered my thoughts again. I put my handbag down and called Nora. When I heard the voice of the care home owner, Jane, I knew things had changed since my last call.

"Frances, we're going to lose Nora. We thought we lost her yesterday. She will probably be gone by the end of today."

"Can she take my call? Is she conscious?" I asked.

"Yes."

She put the phone next to Nora's ear. "Nora?" I asked, after hearing shuffling sounds in the background. Jane came on the telephone again.

"Nora just expired as I put the phone to her ear."

"Nora."

I lighted a red candle for a few minutes, then drove out to my appointment. A few blocks before the medical center, five birds appeared in front of my car. One bird separated from the rest and slowly dipped and soared three times, wings wide apart, then joined the flock and they were gone. Nora's scarf arrived a few weeks later and as expected, it was red. ༄

A Red Umbrella

A red umbrella
Moves across the overpass.
I smile as I sit
In traffic below.
Is it a child
Late for school
Or did Mary Poppins
Get lost in flight?
Such frivolous thoughts
As I drive my mother
To adult day care.

Sometimes, there's nothing left but humor. Yes, bring on the funny bone, the humor cavalry and share the stories with others—there is such release through laughter. We need to turn our spine into a loose rubber band instead of having it stretched beyond its capacity. If we can find the humor in the situation, we can overcome it.

Humor, Imagination and Storytelling

·CHAPTER EIGHT·

BM is a topic that caregivers talk a lot about and on the surface, there doesn't seem to be anything funny about it. The first time is always the most traumatic. When it happened to me, I had walked into my mother's bathroom at 3 a.m. and was met with BM on the floor. In that moment of panic, I grabbed my toothbrush and began scrubbing the floor. I thought, *Maybe there's a poem here.* The minute I said that, I was no longer a poor caregiver scrubbing BM off the floor but was a poet-caregiver and that made all the difference as I began seeking that poem. I found laughter. The result is "A Feather Boa and a Toothbrush" (page 180).

When our efforts to communicate with our loved ones lead to frustrating answers, there's humor to be found. I said in Chapter Six ("Conversations: Can We Talk?"), sometimes we have to wonder who's really having the communication problem. During a visit to the doctor, instead of feeling disappointed in my mother's failure to "pass the test," I looked for something to make me laugh and I did. The result is "Diagnosis: Genius Rejected" (page 183).

Imagination and storytelling also become tools in the caregiver's arsenal. I told myself many stories during caregiving to help make me take deep breaths when the days and nights became too long and unpredictable. I got up each morning and thought, *This could be my mother's last day on earth. How can I not make her last day as pleasant as possible?* So when she hid her soiled clothing in the closet, I said, "She did this to relieve me of having more work cleaning. This was the only way she knew how to help me." When I found her shoes covered with BM on our way out to adult care, I turned her around and said, "God doesn't want us on the freeway right now," and we began the day all over again with gratitude.

I once wrote a journal entry describing a morning commute to my mother's day care:

> *I was stuck in traffic with my mother at my side near an overpass. I was stuck in more ways than one. We sat in the car near an overpass, her voice repeating over and over, "Where am I going?" I sat and watched this woman walk across the overpass, carrying a black umbrella. I sat there and thought, "Now if that woman had a red umbrella, it would create a lovelier image. Red against that blue sky. Better yet, if a child was walking with that umbrella, I would see only the red umbrella walking." These thoughts took the edges off the traffic jam, the looming high rises and my mother's repetitive voice of concern. I soon continued my drive to adult day care.*

Letting my imagination drift gave me the space I needed to regroup and be a better, more patient caregiver. This journal entry, transformed with even more imagination, eventually became a poem, "A Red Umbrella" (page 176), which I often use as an example of how a poem can focus on one small aspect. For more on writing technique, see Chapter Four ("Caregiver into Poet-Caregiver").

My imagination often turned Alzheimer's into a physical being, a thief who had snuck into our lives and stolen what belonged to us. Turning the disease into a villain who could be addressed gave me a focus for many poems. "The Playground" (page 185) and "Dylan Thomas…" (page 186) are two.

For some of us, when caregiving draws to an end, the question of our own mortality begins to nag. *Am I next? Will I get Alzheimer's?* Humor, mixed with contemplation, can help with these thoughts, too. My poem "Spell World Backwards" (page 188) is an example. Sometimes, a little creativity can go a long way. ❧

It is 3 a.m.

I am on my hands and knees

With toothbrush in one hand,

A glass of hot tap water in my other,

Scrubbing BM off my mother's
Bathroom floor.

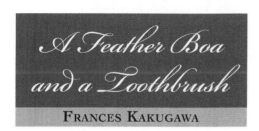

A Feather Boa and a Toothbrush

FRANCES KAKUGAWA

Before a flicker of self-pity can
set in,

A vivid image enters my mind.

An image of a scarlet feather boa

Impulsively bought from Neiman Marcus,

Delicately wrapped in white tissue

Awaiting in my cedar chest

For some enchanted evening.

The contrast between my illusional lifestyle of feather boas,

Opium perfume and black velvet

And my own reality of toothbrushes,

Bathroom tiles and BM at 3 a.m.

Overwhelms me with silent laughter.

At the Market:
Her T-shirt's inside out,
A label sticks out at her nape
Displaying not Polo, Liz or Jones N.Y.

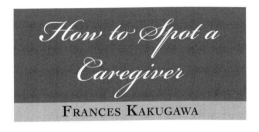

But her size, medium.
Her mother pushing the cart
Looks like an ad
For this month's *Vogue*.

At the Doctor's Office:
A well-coiffed mother
A soft fragrance of Jergens soap
Pleasantly reveals a recent bath.
Her caregiver's roots, inches of gray
A loud cry for L'Oréal
For she's definitely worth it.
Or is she running an ad
For a deodorant?

At the Mall:
The mother in a wheelchair
Coordinated picture-perfect
In a colorful mu'umu'u,
Matching vest and shoes.
Don't look down
But her caregiver's feet in two different sandals
Of two different heights.
But shhhhh, don't tell her,
She needs her dignity preserved, too.

At End of Day:
Peacefully she curls
Into her fetal position,
A half smile playing on her face.
The other, a wet dishrag,
A three-day-old banana peel,
A marathon runner at the finish line,
Ready for another sleepless night.
Good night? ✻

Untitled

RED SLIDER

Only ritual marks the day
in the days that have lost
all trace of beginning or end
in this night without end.

Each day I keep my watch,
by night I sift through ashes,
"Surely, somewhere in all of this
must be the hand of God?"

Caregiver: I sifted through the ashes today and, indeed
found that the hand of God was in there, after all.

Social Worker: And what did you do then?

Caregiver: Handed Him a subpoena for a product liability
lawsuit. ✻

Anxious like a mother with a preschooler,
Hoping for entrance to nursery school,
I sit next to my mother with a silent prayer:
"Please answer all the questions wisely."

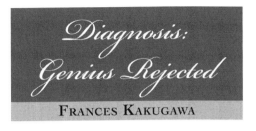

FRANCES KAKUGAWA

"Mrs. Kakugawa,"
the diagnostician begins,
"What is your name?
Where were you born?
How many children do you have?"

Ah, good, good, she's passing with flying colors.

I keep my eyes on his chart,
Checking to see that he marks
The right column, noting Pass.
Positive. Normal.

He upgrades his questioning to:
"Mrs. Kakugawa, you are at Las Vegas airport.
You have lost your airline tickets and it's time to go home.
You have only three dollars. What will you do?"

Without hesitation my mother says,
"I'll put the money back in the slot machine,
Make plenty money and buy another ticket."
She's a genius, I'm applauding silently.

I watch his pencil move to negative on her chart.
Yes, she should have said, "Use a telephone and like ET,
Call home."
Her ingenuity has no place on this chart.

"Mrs. Kakugawa," he continues.
"You're walking down the street and you find a letter.
It has an address and a stamp on.
Tell me what you'll do with this letter."
Once again my genius in disguise answers,
"I'll check the address and deliver it to the house."
Of course she will. She knows all her neighbors.
Another great step for her brain cells.

Wrong. He marks negative on her chart.
"Increase her Aricept."
I walk my mother out, saddened
That geniuses are off his chart.

"How did I do?" she asks,
"Do I have to pay him? Do I have money?"
"You did super good," I say.
"And no, you don't have to pay him.
He should pay you!" ✎

If you let this thief
Get hold of you,
He'll take you
On a merry-go-round.

The Playground

FRANCES KAKUGAWA

Round and round you'll go,
Whirling in orbit.
You can't get off
Till the horses all die down.

If you let this thief
Get hold of you,
On to a seesaw he'll lure you,
Up and up and up
Oh so high the breezes kiss,
And as you suck that breath of life
Down you fall to the ground,
Down and down and down.

If you let this thief
Get hold of you,
He'll lure you out to play,
And soon earth's gravity
Will disown you
Upside down and nowhere to go.
While this thief in disguise
Awaits another day. ✢

When it is all over
I will shout so all can hear.

"We put up a great fight, didn't we?

Dylan Thomas, We Did Not Go Gentle Into the Good Night

FRANCES KAKUGAWA

We didn't just sit back and cower with fear,

We didn't just sit back and curse this thief
As he quietly stole into our lives.
We knew he was cleverer than us,
His presence so mysteriously elusive
To the men in science. We knew his capture
Would not be in your lifetime
But we didn't sit in quiet desperation, did we?
We knew, didn't we, if I had succumbed
To the burden of care, the thief's laughter would have
Echoed through the walls of our home, and soon,
They would have crumbled.
Had you thrown up your arms in hopelessness
Each time the thief had come, he would have triumphed
Oh, so easily.
But we transcended this thief, you and I.
You held your dignity to the very end.

You walked, sometimes stumbled,
But never did you crawl before this monster thief,

No matter how he distanced you
From who and what you were. Relentless as he was,
He could not rob you of all your memory.
You recalled your childhood and the first family
Who had loved you so, leaving him baffled and dumb.
Every inch of the way, you fought smiling, transcending
Each of the indignities he left in his wake.

Had we waited idly in darkened rooms,
For the capture of this thief,
This battle of our human spirit would have been lost.
We called him by name, Alzheimer's,
Thus weakening him with each call.
His Achilles heel we wrapped
With our own pursuit of the Divine.
Whatever he stole, we lived without.
There will be no Nobel Prize for what we did,
Oh, but how we triumphed hour after hour, day after day.
We turned that 36-hour day into a 24-hour day.
We did, didn't we?
With love, dignity, compassion,
Endurance and respect for the human soul,
No match for any prize of any name.
Unattainable by any thief of any size."

When this is over,
Oh, how I will shout in triumph
For the two of us.
Yes! ༄

When that day arrives
When I'm not able to spell "world" backwards
Or recall any of the words given to me in a series,
When that day arrives

Spell World Backwards
FRANCES KAKUGAWA

When I'm not able
to reproduce
Geometric drawings
Of triangles

overlapping rectangles,
And not know the day of my birth,
When that day arrives
When the word "Alzheimer's"
Is whispered behind my back,
And Aricept is prescribed,
I'll go out and have some real fun.
Oh yes, I know the secret, you see.
The people all around me will be told,
"It's the illness, it's not her."
Those words will be my ticket to freedom.
Freedom to do all things I've been taught never to do
But always wanted to:

I will spit in public
From high places or on sidewalks.
I will yawn in church, doze
Or even take a nap.

"It's the disease," they'll say,
"Just let her be."

I'll dress in purple and red,
Stripes against polka dots.
Why not socks of different colors,
Red on my left, green on my right.
That'll be okay, wouldn't it
In December near the 25th?

I'll wear tattered underwear.
So what if the paramedics
Don't find Clorox white lacy ones
Should I get hit crossing the street?

I'll dress each finger
With a ring or two
Bracelets on both wrists
That will jangle and clash.

I'll insist on dessert
Before my entrée
Bacon, eggs and rice
For my cholesterol count.

How about my elbow
On the table,
Do a Jack Benny
To rest between bites?

Smoke a cigarette
On a long, slim, silver holder
Like Miss Davis

On silent screen.

No more responses
To every question.
Why I'll just ignore people
At my will.
"It's the disease," they'll say,
"Just let her be."

I'll pick flowers
From my garden
And pass them out
To strangers with sour faces.

I'll send Christmas cards in July,
Gifts for no reason at all.
And smile at strangers
With "Have a great life."

I will have my fun
Until the day
They no longer say,
"Just let her be." ✤

Humor, Imagination and Storytelling

Family Dynamics

Earthquakes of human existence,
arrive unannounced
First, the gentle trembling under one's feet…
Followed by uncontrollable rocking,
crescendoing into destruction…
Dislodging family heirlooms, soon shattered
on floors and shelves…
Still, the shaking continues like dice in a gambler's hand…
then stillness once again; among the ruins.

We associate "family" with holiday gatherings where there is laughter, oneness and gaity. This is what family is perceived to be—until caregiving is needed. That same family around holiday tables may not be so unified and cooperative when a member is diagnosed with

Alzheimer's disease. To expect each family member to rise to caregiving may not be a reality. To expect equal participation, interest and commitment may not be a reality. Caregiving is long term and many may choose not to participate and for the sake of the one needing care, it's best to not coerce anyone into caregiving. Caregivers and the loved ones need all the positive support they can get, which can come in many different forms, from financial aid to help with household chores. In many instances "family" may need to be redefined.

Not everyone is cut out to be a caregiver, so be honest if you feel that you cannot handle the demands of being a caregiver and give help in other ways. If you are unable to become an active caregiver, there are many other ways you can help. The following are some suggestions I offered in my "Dear Frances" column in *The Hawai'i Herald*. Ask the caregiver about:

- Finances: Contribute your share of expenses.

- Household Chores: Pay for someone to do house cleaning or to take care of the yard.

- Carpentry: Work to make the house safe and Alzheimer's-friendly.

You can also:

- Express and show gratitude: For example, give gift cards for restaurants, massages, manicures, etc.

- Join a support group to learn about the disease and the demands it places on the caregiver so that you will have a better understanding of the situation. Educate yourself about the disease and its symptoms so that you will be able to converse on the same wavelength.

Once it has been settled which family members will be responsible for day-to-day caregiving, one of the biggest conflicts that arise tends to be over the level of care provided. Unless you live with the person being cared for, you will not know what caregiving encompasses. Telephone conversations with loved ones reveal very little because of social graces. My mother had a standard conversation:

Okasan: "Hello…"
Caller: "Long time no see. How are you?"
Okasan: "Oh, I'm fine."

This conversation did not give a clue as to where she was in the stages of the disease, nor the demands being made of the caregiver. Asking questions requiring very little memory tells us hardly anything about the state of their dementia. For example:

Caller: "Did you have breakfast?"
Loved one: "Yes."
Caller: "How are you doing?"
Loved one: "Good."
Caller: "What are you going to do today?"
Loved one: "Oh, not much."

Family members should not judge so easily that the caregiver is exaggerating about the loved one's decline just because the telephone conversation seems so normal. On the other hand, non-caregivers should not be too quick to think that the situation is out of control if confronted by "abnormal" behavior. Remember the Two Worlds — the caregiver and loved one may have discovered a way to keep peace and dignity in ways that seem odd to an outsider.

I often felt that it was too much of a bother to explain to someone else how to give care to my mother because she was so used to me. But just because a family member was unable to take on the role of primary caregiver, does not mean they cannot be a part of the caregiving experience at all. Allow them to assist you in the ways that they are able. We often feel that others will not be able to give care like we do because of the structure and schedule we have established, but remember that there is not only one way to provide care for your loved one. When a sibling helps with caregiving, try to get out of the house, don't micromanage—ideally, take a vacation when they're visiting. Write out the schedule for your siblings to follow, as change will confuse the one being cared for. A list with the following information will help:

- Physician's name, office phone number (cell, if available) and address

- Names and phone numbers of people who may have to be called upon in the event of a crisis (plumber, electrician, medical personnel, neighbors, friends, etc.)

- Shower/bath time

- Meal times

- Outings

- Favorite foods, TV shows, music and activities

Finally, in a family with an Alzheimer's patient in the mix, where are our children? Too often we isolate our children from the elderly as a means of protection. In my work with children, they constantly show their capability to embrace those they love, regardless of age or illness. My children's book, *Wordsworth Dances the Waltz*, deals with exactly this topic. Both children and adults benefit from interaction. Bring a child into the room, and watch that spark light in the eyes of the elderly. Many schools create yearlong programs in which students visit nursing facilities. The bond developed between those children and the elderly patients is heartwarming. What better way to help our children get in touch with their own humanity? ✦

I was full of resentment.

Life was anchored in resentments.

Resentments ate away at me

Fueling my unhappiness and rage.

Resentment

LINDA NAGATA

Why was I expected to "take care of"
everything?

Didn't others see they could help?

Why did others ask what they could do to help, and not
follow through?

My resentments built, one incident after another.

I felt entitled to hold these resentments

Take them out and mull them over, and over, and over

See what a good person I am, I do everything

Others set me up and expect me to "take care of"

I set myself up and expect myself to "take care of."

Later I learned I couldn't control other people,
places or things.

I can only do what I can do for myself

Expecting my family to help allows them to have power
over me.

How freeing to have learned this lesson. ✒

My head throbs with stress,

Aches from dealing with this mess.

I hate tonight.

One of the sinister menagerie of emotions

Spawned by Alzheimer's disease.

Stress

JODY MISHAN

It eats away at our hearts.

It sucks the marrow of our strength.

Our immune system and adrenaline

Goes into overdrive and malfunctions.

Coping with crisis after crisis.

Mess after mess.

It takes its toll.

Anger tonight.

I rage at Hawai'i.

A state that's still in the Dark Ages,

In not having progressive, accessible or affordable

Alzheimer's facilities.

I rage at my father

Who had not the foresight that this might happen.

For leaving me with

Dysfunctional remnants of our family,

This disease has destroyed

The fragile little family we did have.

Turning siblings into enemies.

It is only me who is left to be responsible for him,

Because no one else will sacrifice.

I rage that life was stripped of all its splendor,
One appendage at a time.
Each dissection left me with a few functioning parts,
So it didn't seem so bad.
But now there's hardly anything left.
And I'm exhausted, uninspired, too numb
To renew my spirit.
Just needing rest.

I finally look back and see all the wrong turns,
And that I can't turn back.
It's too late.
But going forward seems barren, short, unexciting.
Not worth pursuing the future anymore,
Not with this heavy burden.

Is the caregiving killing me?
This fear is always there.
I beg God to help me through these dark times.
To give me strength.
If I did not have prayer at times like this
I could not have made it this far. ༺

Today…only **black, white and gray**…
Parched wastelands of humanity
Barren, sizzling in hot summer.
Black vultures circling above,

across crayoned fields.

FRANCES KAKUGAWA

*This poem came to me as a series of
strong images while listening to a caregiver tell the story of her sisters' interest
in their mother's finances while they
refused to participate in her care. The
caregiver's cry, "But we are sisters!" as
she expressed her confusion and grief
called to me.*

Waiting for a last breath…
White porcelain faces of sisters
Uttering their inability to
become human…
Gray where hope, prayer
and beliefs
In human goodness linger
For half a second
Before dissipating into reality
Of what is. **Black. White.** ❧

Where have all the children gone
They came for candy and ice cream
to pet Bella and run their fingers over
her silky fur then screamed with

delight as Bella kissed away morsels
of ice cream from their lips.

Bob Oyafuso

They came to sit with Grandma
or to watch an artist at work
and learn from the master
the art of drawing.

They came for Grandma's
unconditional love and attention.

Then came Alzheimer's and
now she is strange and distant
Grandma can only smile at them.
The house is silent. ✺

When Grandma hugged me
And said, "How's my Wordsworth?"

When Grandma sent me presents

Grandma

From *Wordsworth Dances the Waltz*

FRANCES KAKUGAWA

On special days of the year,

When Grandma gave me candy
Right before dinner time,

When Grandma told me stories
Way past my bedtime,

She was Grandma to me
Because she was Grandma,

Not because she had a memory
Or because she knew my name.

Now that she's losing her memory,
She's still my Grandma, isn't she? ✒

Grandparents,
You are like that trunk of an oak
Whose roots grow deep into our soil
Sending branches up to the skies.

Grandparents Day
From *Wordsworth Dances the Waltz*

FRANCES KAKUGAWA

You are a book without end,
Filled with stories and folklore
Of when you were a child

Long before we were born.

You are a treasure
On our treasure hunt,
Gold, trinkets and gems
Where X marks the spot.

Grandparents,
Your stories, your memories,
We will preserve and treasure
For our children and their children.

Grandparents,
We honor you
On this day. ⁂

Memo #1-2-3
From: Frances Kakugawa
Subject: Nursing Homes

#1: Put me in a nursing facility with my blessings, without guilt. Do honor my health directives and living trust on my end-of-life wishes.

This decision is for both of us so relax and do what seems right in the reality of what is.

#2: Laugh at my babbling. I was never good at language with my Pidgin talk. Finally, a medical reason for my incomprehensible gobbledegook.

#3: Two more requests: Do not give me that "nursing home haircut." I wore that *chawan* (rice bowl) cut enough times in my childhood. Oh, and my first choice is an all-male nursing home. But I'll settle for whatever is available. I hope you are laughing.

Life is just right.

There comes a time when the only alternative is to place our loved ones in a nursing facility. This may cause feelings of guilt and remorse because somewhere in our minds is that voice saying, "Don't put me away." Visitations with loved ones in nursing facili-

Put Me in a Nursing Home

·CHAPTER TEN·

ties can often turn into a ride on an emotional seesaw as we sec-ond-guess our decisions based on what transpires during each visit. A conversation such as the one my mother and I had throughout her life, may make such transi-tions less painful for caregivers:

Okāsan: When I get old, just put me in a nursing home and you don't need to visit me.
Me: Naah, I'll take care of you at home. If you're nice, I'll give you nice warm baths. But if you get nasty, I'll hose you down with cold water in the garage for your baths.
Laughter.

Yes, we teased and laughed a lot about her later years, but the message was clear: she gave me permission to put her in a nurs-ing home with a health directive, and when the time came for that placement, I recalled with gratitude, those conversations. And it was very okay for both of us. Of course, this placement would never be totally free of remorse and sadness. I wrote "Dear Caregiver" (page 210) to give myself affirmation that this was truly my mother's message to me.

The poems in this section express sorrow, guilt and sadness. I tried to overcome my own sadness by focusing on my view of my mother as a woman. When I visited, I joked about setting her up with one of the male residents—this brought laughter. We talked about life outside the facility. I made sure, to the very end, that she was a woman first, not a mother whose daughter placed her in a nursing home. I didn't spend each visit feeding my guilt; we laughed and teased a lot and spent our time together in a world of joy and liveliness.

When my mother died, the entire nursing home staff stood in silence outside her room, against the wall in a line. Many had tears on their faces. This relationship between my mother and the staff was consciously developed so whenever they saw my mother, they also saw me. And who was I?

I was that person who showed appreciation for their care of my mother by becoming one of them. Complaints, I felt, would be attached to my mother so I built my own relationship with the staff, filled with positive reinforcements. My mother's hair was always combed with flowers in them. Her face made up with blush and lipstick. I felt someone was finding joy in caring for her. Here are a few of the things I did to foster a better relationship with the care staff: left flowers on the front desk, kept snacks in their lounge, helped to feed other residents, folded the laundry with the women residents, "took over" the bulletin board by the elevator with holiday themes, carved pumpkins for Halloween, put up a Christmas tree, ran a Christmas door decorating contest for families. On a more advanced level, I ran sessions for the staff to work on combining professional skills with more compassionate care. For example, we fed each other and the aides discovered how difficult it was to swallow food when someone is shoving food into your mouth. I also worked with administration for the dismissal of an aide whose behavior was of danger to the well-being of the residents. Most importantly, however, I reminded them often how I depended upon them to be the family I couldn't be when my mother was in their care.

Matsue had me,
Iris had John,°
Ronnie had Nancy,
Who will I have

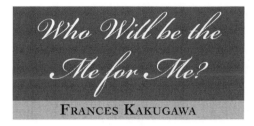

Who Will be the Me for Me?

FRANCES KAKUGAWA

When I grow old?
My options are many
So I never lose sleep
On who will be me for me.

Option One:
    I will find a younger man
    Many springs to my autumn.
    A nurse's aide, preferably
    Like young Ernesto at
    My mother's care facility.

Option Two:
    I will sacrifice my original plan
    Hanging around country clubs for wealthy men,
    But will stick to nurses' lounges
    At UC Davis Medical or Kaiser Permanente,
    Find not one but a dozen friends
    All young, crisp RNs.

Option Three:
    I will go to South Carolina
    Where prisons cater to Alzheimer's inmates,
    Those lifers have aged without parole.

I'll rob a bank in that city
Be housed forever in their Alzheimer's section
With murderers, rapists and terrorists,
All without memory.

Which will it be?
My first would be an Ernesto
Who'd be strong with wheelchairs and Hoyer lifts.
With our language barrier, he won't hear
All my vulgarity in Japanese.
I will be speaking Japanese, won't I?
But if all fails, I'll return
To the most sensible, already in print:
A long-term care insurance,
A nursing home under Frances Tapat,
A health directive
And God as my Me. ✣

°*Iris is writer Dame Murdoch, and John is her husband, John Bayley*

I am a burden,
Whether the sun greets you
From ocean blue skies,
On a picture-perfect morn.

Dear Caregiver

FRANCES KAKUGAWA

I am a burden,
Whether you gulp in this near
perfection
To make it yours,

Forgetting for a moment
I am here.

I am a burden,
Whether dark clouds
Hover over the city,
Forecasting rain
On a Sunday afternoon,
Filling you with an ache
That has no name at all,
I am a burden.

Whether the moon is full or new
In this house that is silenced
By fragmented sleep,
I am a burden.

We live with two thieves, you and I,
And I have become the greater thief
Chiseling away at you

Inch by inch, hour by hour,
Turning you into a kaleidoscope.

Alzheimer's, my nemesis,
No one can yet destroy
But the thief that I have become
Can be expunged.
Free yourself from this thief
With the bond that once existed.
Squeezing out urine from carpets and bedding,
Scrubbing bathroom tiles at 3 a.m.,
Staying up nights, answering his constant calls,
Using your diminishing strength to transport
A thief almost twice your size
Is an act of pure sacrifice,
An act that shatters me like fallen crystal.
It is no longer an act of love,
But one of burden.

We were not joined by blood or vows
For this kind of loving.
The thief has left me with needs
Anyone not bearing your name can meet.
The love that I needed, you have given
Before there was a thief.

We have bade farewell, you and I,
When there was a me.

Let me go before you begin
To crawl in debris of self-destruction.
Set me free in a nursing home
Where the thief I have become
Can no longer be.

To your courage, your love and loyalty
To want to rise above the burden of care,
I press my palms together to you.
But listen to my unspoken words,
It's time to be free.
Free from guilt, sorrow,
Physical and spiritual destruction.
Let us both know peace.
Return us to who we were. ❧

My Mother, My Child

LINDA DONAHUE

Old photograph,
circa 1949,
one moment frozen in time
on a Kodachrome slide.

There's Mom toddling me,
firstborn daughter, on her knee.
She beams at me adoringly
while I gaze away,
straight into the camera,
sober and serious,

as if I'd already traveled
time's long corridors and returned,
burdened with prescience
of all that lay ahead.

As I matured, Mom
grew distant, uncertain.
All my irksome *nevers*
lined up against her normalcy:
I never played with dolls,
never babysat,
never had or wanted kids,
and never understood
those who did.

It was more than disinterest.
I was unfit for the only
kind of life Mom knew.
Unfit for motherhood
with its constant monitoring
of bodily functions, its demands and cares,
the commitment and self-sacrifice required.
I knew I could never do it.
Yet all my vows of *never*
came to naught.
My ninety-year-old child
relies on me for all the motherlies
I couldn't give in younger years.
Today she eyed me quizzically:

Do I know you?
I think so.
You're the nice one,
the one who helps me.
Those others are so mean.

Mom thinks I work at her residence.
I straighten her closet and dresser —
they're always a mess —
comb her hair, brush her teeth,
check her diaper, powder her yeast,
take her for walks, massage her feet,
cream her onion-paper skin,
bring her treats (she's getting so thin!),
shop for her clothes, whatever she needs,
pay her bills, manage her assets,
do all I can to comfort and cheer her.

When I leave she thanks me,
adding, as an afterthought:
if you see my girls,
tell them to visit me.
They never come anymore. ✿

On a quiet Saturday evening,
I join my friend in the dining room
Of her residence in a new retirement home,
Advertised as one of the most plush residences

Noh Drama

FRANCES KAKUGAWA

Noh Drama is a style of Japanese stage play using masks.

In the city.
I sit and watch, porcelain masks:
On a man in a wheelchair,
On two women slow dancing the shuffle
Led by their walkers,
A couple gingerly entering the room,
Not as debonair Englishmen,
But simply, two old men with canes.
A few join visiting family members

For the last supper of the day.
All with porcelain masks,
Smiling at their grown children
Also masked in smiles.
I can almost hear
Their voices of affirmation:
Yes, this was the right thing to do.
Everyone is happy, happy.
Freedom not to cook, clean or scrub,
Freedom not to water their flowers,
Or dine from their garden.
Freedom not to live
In houses etched with memories.
Yes, this was the right thing to do.
Freedom.

After supper, they wait silently for the elevator.
What do they do after the doors close?
What do they do in their rooms?
Do they take their masks off
At their doors and lay them aside?
Or do they go to bed masked,
Hoping to become one with each painted smile?
I should have ordered dessert. ✎

Waiting

LINDA DONAHUE

she sits at bed's edge
glaring, jaw clenched:
who are you?
my girls never visit

the babies are lost
I'll be in trouble
nobody tells me what
I'm supposed to do
do you live here?
does my mom know I'm here?
can you call her?
my dad has a car
he'll take me home
what is this place?
strange men get
under the bed
they don't talk right
they say bad things about me

this is turning into
a store tomorrow
where will I go?
did my mom call you?
could I live with you?
I could take care of you
I could be your nurse
I could wash your dishes
you'd better go now
my dad is trying to find me…
…who are you?

she doesn't know me,
her firstborn daughter
she sits at bed's edge
glaring, jaw clenched
laundry basket beside her
packed with random clothing
and remnants of a vanished life
waiting for her world
to make sense again
waiting, unsuspecting,
in Alzheimer's shadow.

I Wish You Could Stay

LINDA DONAHUE

As usual, we walk together to the front door at visit's end.

Mom's headlong shuffling gait and flat affect
    announce Alzheimer's, stage five.

As usual, I give Mom a big hug and kiss,
    expecting her to turn around and march off to lunch
    before I'm out the door, no memory I was there.
But today she holds me and doesn't let go.
Tears etch channels down her cheeks.
I ask what's troubling her, why she's crying.
She responds in a whisper,
    This is the last time I'll see you, isn't it.
    I wish you could stay.
Her quiet certainty sounds an alarm in my heart.
Startled, I promise her it's not the last time,
    I'll be back tomorrow.
But Mom doesn't hear my assurances.
She focuses her gaze on my face, intent, penetrating,
    as if to fix my image in the darkroom of her heart.

As usual, my brain rummages for understanding.
Does she suspect she's entering uncharted territory,
    leaving behind every loved one, everything familiar?
Can she sense it's the last time she'll recognize me?
Is *she* the one who wants to stay?

Or has anxiety written another terrifying script
        and tricked her into believing it?
I'll never know, she'll never know, and it doesn't matter.
Her earlier disturbing emotions are already forgotten.

As usual, I wave with feigned cheer as I drive away,
        knowing there **will** be a last time soon, if not today.
Soon, if not tomorrow, I won't be Mom's daughter.
My arm around her shoulders drawing her close,
        my warm hand thawing her bony blue fist,
        will offer the solace of a stranger, nothing more.

As always, I'll grieve silently behind the smiling strength
        I conjure for her.
And love her still, even when she doesn't know me. ❧

What is Death?

When does a loved one truly die?
I look at her obituary
And it doesn't seem real
To see the word "died"
Next to her name.
Do obituaries tell the truth?
I look at the list of names
Under "In Memoriam"
In *Mosaic Moon*,
I stop at the date of her death,
I read her name, Matsue Kakugawa
And I wonder, is she really gone?
I take a mental journey through
All the spaces she had filled
And question What is death?
Shouldn't my mind, too,
Be purged of all its memories and images,
My heart of all emotional ties?
Shouldn't death also occur
In these parts of me
That still feel her presence?
What is death?

There was no preparation for that moment when my mother took her last breath. The script was all wrong. When I was told her blood pressure was lowering, I didn't know that medically, it meant she was dying. I left to take a shower and a few min-

On Death and Dying

· C H A P T E R   E L E V E N ·

utes after I left, she drew her last breath. And with that, my orchestrated plan of having my hand in hers when she died, ended.

Soon afterward, I was moving like a robot in trance, attending to the logistics of death: calls to ministers, funeral parlor, family, and friends. It also felt brutally final to see or say the words "died" and "death." It seemed gentler to use "passing" or other synonyms, and yet, whatever words I used, I discovered through time, death is not final, for the life that it held is still a process inside of me. Perhaps that life has more staying power than that one second of death. Some things, like Alzheimer's disease and dying, can't be fixed, nor can we control them, but we can try to make some sense of them without any answers if we listen to the silence to get out of the world of chaos and sounds.

There are infinite methods of caregiving, unique as the many families in the world, and just as many ways to grieve. The process is very personal and individualized, with its own time line. When Eugenie Mitchell's mother died, we sat together in her living room without talking. We both understood, without saying, how meaningful the moment was.

When Setsuko Yoshida lost her husband, our support group sat around a table, knowing there was no need for words—and there were none that could be offered. It was not the time for clichés (*He is in a better place, she is no longer suffering*, etc.) or to extend one's own personal religious beliefs.

There is comfort in knowing we are not expected to bring closure to our feelings and to our new environment immediately after memorial or funeral services. There is an enormous amount of sorting awaiting us both in our emotional and physical lives.

The death of both parents means we no longer have a place to return home to on holidays and special occasions. This physical change brings new family designs; who will replace a parent's home on the holidays? Will this disintegrate the family unit that was so important to our parents? Did we bury our family traditions, folklore and myths along with our parents? The tug-of-war continues, with our wanting someone to say, "Death is not the end."

In the sorting process, we also find comfort in the artifacts and other forms of memorabilia left by our loved ones. Here is a way to hold on to a life that is gone, giving us solace. When I found my mother's handkerchief, I held on to it until I wrote a poem, "Handkerchief" (page 245). Interestingly, once I wrote the poem, I was ready to let go of that handkerchief. Linda Nagata, whose poem "Decoration" (page 243) expresses the near-physical sensation of memories when we encounter their posessions, also wrote after her mother's death: "I feel your presence watching me, sharing with me, the pleasure of creating. This ongoing bond, it comforts me."

So we allow each person to grieve in his or her own way—there is no specific prescription. Let grieving take its natural course as we live our new post-caregiving lives. ✤

my tap root

    no longer

        embraces me…

Going Home with Thomas Wolfe

FRANCES KAKUGAWA

my tap root

    is slowly fading away…

        like photos in old

albums…

soon,

    that tap root

will no longer be…

i

    can

        almost

            hear

                its

                    final

                        gasp… ❧

First Dry Run:

I am a balloon suddenly released from the hands of a child,
Soaring high above concrete streets, man-made walls, rooftops,
Beyond what my eyes can see.

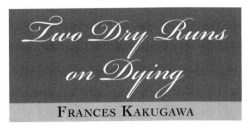

Two Dry Runs on Dying

FRANCES KAKUGAWA

I am, within minutes, my mother's child
Suddenly transformed into a
mature adult,
Capable, responsible, in control of what
I was destined to be.

A desire to shout my revelations, my discovery, my arrival
Silently accompanies me alone to the parking garage.
How can I feel such elation, such freedom, such joy
When minutes ago I had said, "Yes, Doctor,
It's time to let her go.
No more treatments and tests.
If we revive her, it'll be for the nursing home.
What quality of life will that be?
I need to respect her living will and her wishes.
It's time to let her go."

My mother's doctor hands me one of her tissues.
Our eyes meet without words, a hug, then departure.
All rehearsals done, script memorized.
It is opening night.

I cry myself out in the shower, not for the decision I had made,
Not for the death sentence I had proclaimed,
But for that time that had arrived to honor my mother's living will.
It was a decision easier to come to
Than "Do I take her to ER for her rectal bleeding?
Or shall I wait until Monday morning?
Do I call her doctor about her fever
Or do I give her liquids instead?"

These daily decisions were mine to make,
A responsibility synonymous with caregiving.
Decisions concerning her living will were not mine to make.
I was but a mere voice of her will,
Made years before the thief's invasion.

The next morning my mother revives herself.
I smile and chuckle, "If this were a test,
I have passed with flying colors.
Ah, a mother to the very near end."

Second Dry Run:

Her quiet rambling voice leads me directly to her.
She is lying on her recliner, eyes closed, face peaceful,
Her mouth moving nonstop.

I lean over to hear her words.
Her Japanese is not of her usual vernacular

But of a more formal dialect used with ministers.

She has slipped into her spiritual world.
She is speaking to her dead mother.
"Oh, Mother, don't you know I'm here?
Of course I'm here. I told you I was coming.
I may have been stupid but I don't think I was bad.
Yes, yes, I have come to be with you."
She soon takes her mother's voice:

"Oh, Matsue, you have come.
I'm so glad you are here.
I told you not to worry, didn't I?
I told you everything would be all right.
There is nothing to worry about, nothing to fear.
I am here."

Her voice then becomes the observer,
Describing a scene of such joy, I, too, feel the joy.
She is being hugged by her mother.
Such joy, so much love.
Matsue is leaping and dancing with joy.

A Buddhist sutra follows.
The entire scenario is repeated
She lifts her hand outward reaching toward someone.
She wants to go somewhere but can't find her way.
I gently nudge her to awaken her.

She opens her eyes, looks at me and shouts with recognition,
"Hideko," then slips into her spiritual world.
Her voice begins again.

Once again I am given a gift.
A gift to let me see how her final transition will be.
She is being loved and comforted in ways no mortal being
Here on earth could ever love her.
She is leaping and dancing with joy,
Joy no place on earth could ever give her.
I, too, am filled with joy
For I know now, my own perceptions
That without my hand in hers, her final journey
Will begin a lonely journey
Is not of my reality, nor hers.
When she dies, she will not need me.
For that final transition, she will have her beloved mother
And her husband, who are waiting for her
With extended arms.
I am but a mortal being. ᨀ

Caregiver Bio

·JASON KIMURA·

Jason Kimura managed his mother Lillian's care in 2001 after she had a series of strokes. Both he and his father Ronald cared for her over an eight-month period during her steady decline and death. Although she suffered from respiratory difficulties due to tuberculosis as a young adult, she created a loving and untroubled home life for her husband and son. Jason is a writer, graphic designer and photographer who lives in Kailua, Hawai'i. Married for twenty-nine years to his wife Kathy, he has two children. In 2009, he published a book titled *The Queen's Medical Center*, a 150-year history of the hospital that also captures a part of Hawai'i's history, with an emphasis on medicine. Jason enjoys serving at his church, Trinity Presbyterian Church, and its primary mission, Trinity Christian School. His interests also include journaling, reading, painting, drawing, and restoring antiques.

May 9

And so it finally begins. My mother's descent to her final day. It happened on March 10, my mother's stroke. It was unexpected only from a narrow viewpoint. The week before it happened, she received oxygen in her home. We didn't expect the stroke, but her decline was becoming too obvious not to notice. The stroke was an unforeseen detail in her general descent.

But there can be no complaint concerning my mother. When I was a child, we were very close, but there was always a cloud: my mother had just one lung, less than one, actually, due to tuberculosis in the late 1940s. There was no cure then, except surgery, and to wait in the sanitarium at Leahi Hospital, where, in all, she spent seven years. Not yet married to my mother, my father waited for her against hope. They removed the lung tissue; her teeth rotted away. When she was close to death, they had a cure. They gave the medication to her only for comfort, thinking she was too far gone, but it made her well. My parents were married in 1955, and I was born in 1961. Life for them must have been so fragile, precious, but tenuous, like a silk thread.

Even as a child, I recognized my mother's physical weakness. I was always reticent to leave her side, even for an evening, lest she not be there when I returned. Even at the beginning of my teen years, my heart would tug, ache when we were separated for too long. Much later, when we spoke of her condition, she revealed that the doctors had told her what her life expectancy was. She would never tell me what it was, but I knew it was short. (My father recently revealed the dread age to be sixty-five.) At seventy-seven, it is long past. For that I am grateful.

June 17, Father's Day

We had just reached The Queen's Medical Center's lobby. Jonathan and Jenny (the kids), my wife Kathy and I, halfway back to the car, almost free from the burdens of the day, when we heard, "Code 500, Room 956" over the intercom — my mother's room. I raced back to the elevators while Kathy took charge of the kids. By the time I reached the room, some twenty-odd people — doctors, interns, nurses, hospital chaplain, security officer — had assembled at the room, spilling out into the hallway.

I claimed a floor tile just inside the doorway trying not to take up too much space and peered anxiously at my mother, who minutes before had stopped breathing. In the preceding weeks and months, the anxiety had been coming in waves like nausea, each time the phone rings, the pager beeps, a voice on the other end of the line explains a new development. Today during the crisis, the anxiety was mostly at bay, replaced by numbness, or perhaps exhaustion, physical, emotional and spiritual.

There has been a crisis every week. Last week it was sifting through Medicare issues for my parents. The week before that, my mother's heart rate went up to 150 and soul-gutting decisions had to be made on her do-not-resuscitate status. The week before that, she had her tracheotomy put in. The week before that, we asked her if she wanted us to remove the ventilator and let her die (which she refused) because we knew it was never going to come off.

The week before that, she was intubated and put on the ventilator after going into respiratory distress. The week before that, I replaced her internist so she could come to Queen's, where I work, and shortly after was brought to the Queen's ER and admitted for rectal bleeding. The week before that, she was rushed to the Kuakini Medical Center's ER because she could barely breathe. The week before that, she came home from her first hospital stay at Kuakini—a fifty-day stay—and Kathy, my father and I spent eleven hours going back and forth to the pharmacy and other stores for medications and supplies and getting everything in order. The week before that, I went to the hospital on my fortieth birthday to learn from therapists how to be a caregiver.

The week before that, there were conferences with social workers and doctors on my mother's prognosis. The week before that, I heard my mother say for the first time that she wanted to die. The week before that, I had to replace unhelpful hospital personnel. The week before that, my mother was in the progressive care unit, struggling to get off of the ventilator and finally being freed, while we consulted with the family attorney about unhappy choices. The week before that, she was in the intensive care unit and we didn't know what her prognosis was. And finally, the week before that, I had rushed to ER to find her twitching on a gurney, ventilator tube rudely taped down over her mouth and around her head, and a doctor telling me my mother had a serious hemorrhagic stroke, and that this was probably the end. The latest crisis was resolved, and the Code Team left one by one. What will next week's crisis be? What will I do when this is all over?

Tuesday, July 3

I sit with my mother and pretend I am twenty years old and that we have as many good years ahead as behind, that her hospital stay is simply a temporary setback, that the three of us—mom, dad and son—will go on living as we always had. I pretend that this time of togetherness is not temporary like the iridescent colors of a soap bubble, but as permanent as a happy ending forever preserved on celluloid, to be replayed time and again. I wipe saliva from the side of her mouth as casually as I would remove a speck of dust from her blouse. I ignore the ventilator tubes because she sees them not. Instead, I take her hand and hold it reassuringly, pretending not to notice its shaky unsteadiness. She slips her hand out from under mine and puts it on top reassuringly. Perhaps I am no longer twenty, but fifteen, or maybe ten. Either way, I can pretend.

My father called that afternoon to report that my mother had a lot of rectal bleeding. She was, though, he said, very awake and responsive. He asked her if she was happy. She nodded affirmatively. Yes, of course I would go to see her later as usual. It seemed just another medical incident to me—one of many that had been occurring on a regular basis. I worked. I worked a bit more, but intended to break in the middle so seeing her would not be the last late event of the day before heading home. I took a break and procrastinated.

At about 4:15 p.m., my mother's nurse paged me. Her vitals were failing (or did she say destabilizing?) I should come soon. Was she going to die soon? It was hard to tell from the way the nurse said it. There was no urgency in her voice, but I called my father and told him to come. Somehow, nothing seemed to register. It didn't seem like it would be my mother's last day. There was a deep-seated sense of doom, but there was also a shuddering groan within me, like the great beams of timber in the keel of a ship being pummeled by a stormy sea, and the two emotions co-mingled so as to be indistinguishable. I went to the bathroom to relieve myself, to eliminate what weakness I could, and trotted quickly down the halls.

I got to the room at 4:30. My mother was already gone. Her heart has stopped beating, the nurse informed me. The room seemed airless, as in a vacuum. A single tear rolled down my cheek. I took her hand, but could barely hold it, for it was already as cold as death. The ventilator, which had artificially extended my mother's life, still breathed for her, oblivious of the death of its patient, and continued to part her lips with puffs of air at regular intervals. I was mortified at the icy hand and the heedless ventilator. The nurse explained that she was not allowed to turn it off until my mother was pronounced by a doctor, who eventually came in to call the death at 4:25.

Somehow, although we were adrift at sea, my father and I had made it to shore, as I knew we would. And what does one do, who has been adrift for so long, except to crumble on the wet sand like a once sharp-shiny seashell, tumbled and dulled by the surf, thinking nothing of tragedy or loss—in fact thinking of nothing at all—except for the answer to the question of why God did not take her sooner. Each day of her slow descent had been given to my father, who loved her best, so he could, in his own time, let her go. ✣

Saturday, November 3

JASON KIMURA

I am at the edge of
getting past
my mother's long illness,
to see her as she was

in all the years she was well;
but even then,
they are only glimpses. ✣

I love your hands.
The strong, defined veins,
The old, folded skin.
Hands that are good,

Final Moments

JODY MISHAN

Of a good man.
Hands that are now frail from
dying,
And of no use to you any more,

Except for their beauty.

I watch and listen to your body
These final hours of life on this earth.
The last time I can feel your warmth,
Your strong heart beating,
Your wrist and forearm bones
Now delicate and fragile from dying.

You smell sweet.
Your skin is soft,
Your eyes occasionally open
Like bright, magic stars
Fixedly shining, still alive
For a brief time.

I hold your hand,
Stroke your fingers,
Moisten your mouth,
Wipe your forehead.

I wait with you
For your time,
That neither of us
Can rush or delay.

I love you so deeply
That I can't move.
I study the sacred stillness
Just the sound of your breaths,
Their patterns changing.

You no longer have to
Walk the path of Alzheimer's.
Eight years of losses and adjustments.
All met by you
With gentle acceptance, strength, dignity,
Humor, love and a good nature.
There could be no higher level of heroism.

I honor you. I adore you.
I will miss you and your gentle soul
That illness could not touch.

You are my hero,
My dear father.
I have been so blessed
To care for you all this time,
Until the very end, the very last breath,

The moment your soul could fly.

You left me like a feather, like a butterfly,
Soft and peaceful.
gift of love I will treasure forever. ༔

We said our goodbyes long before she was diagnosed with

Alzheimer's. Over dinner one night, in her favorite restaurant, we told each other, should that day come and we are unable to be there, this was our good-bye. And we toasted each other our love and commitment.

So years later…when I returned a minute later with a glass of water in my hand and stood in the doorway, I didn't have to go any nearer to know she had chosen that moment to die—all at once, at home, the way she'd wanted.

Still:

In death, the moonlight,
closer than an empty bed,
an unlit doorway. ༔

at the very end
as it was
at the beginning
i was the child

Her Final Breath

FRANCES KAKUGAWA

she remained the mother
she took hold
of time and place
for her final exit

protecting me
child of her womb

the final severance
of the umbilical cord
made easy and gentle
a final gift
from mother to child

the thief once again
failed in his efforts
to switch our roles
for three years she played along
but in her soul, she was always
the mother. ✢

In Memoriam

FRANCES KAKUGAWA

I tiptoe softly
in the silence of the house
how loud her absence. ✢

Patrick is gone now,
He has returned home
To his spiritual home of homes
To the land of the Buddhas,

Going Home

SETSUKO YOSHIDA

A place where his life began
Even before he was born.

I reflect with fond, loving memories

Fifty years of marriage
To a man solidly grounded
Like the rock of Gibraltar.
Sparse words were spoken to express
His deep-felt feelings,
He showed his emotions
Through kind, thoughtful and simple ways.

Experiences shared of joy, pain and sorrow,
Our son and vegetable gardening
Brought him his greatest joy.
We faced many deaths in our family together
Of mothers, fathers, brothers, sisters,
Of nieces, nephews and friends.

As a soldier fighting in the 442nd combat team,
Three years in Europe during the second world war,
He faced his own mortality
Seeing the lives of his buddies being destroyed
By guns, grenades and artillery fire.

The reality of death made him
See the fragility of life,
Appreciating the gift of his unrepeatable life.
He learned to live fully in the present,
Once saying simply,
"I'm always thinking about life, and
I'm really satisfied with the way my life is."
Each day was a new day and the last day. ৵

The soldiers stood cemented to the grassy ground
Like statues, while Buddhist sutras filled the air.

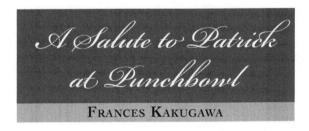

A Salute to Patrick
at Punchbowl

FRANCES KAKUGAWA

Movement would dis-
honor the man who once
stood
In his uniform, like his
comrades today.

The three-gun salute, the wailing taps,
The precision of the folding of the flag,
A salute purified by white gloves
For the presentation of the symbolic flag.

Each step of ultimate precision, a tribute to dignity,
Honor and respect for the fallen soldier,
From the country whom he had served
With love, dignity and honor.

Whatever Alzheimer's had stolen from him,
All was returned to him today.
Whatever memories, forgotten,
The country that he loved, remembered.

A final rest in peace. ✿

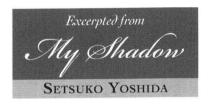

Excerpted from

My Shadow

SETSUKO YOSHIDA

…I call out your name
And talk to you
But you do not answer.
You live in Nirvana now,
Fully enlighted.

You reach out to comfort me
When I'm alone and feeling lonely,
We are always together
Within Boundless Light and Life
Now and forever more. ✿

You are my hero,
My dear father.
I have been so blessed
To care for you all this time,

Untitled

JODY MISHAN

Until the very end, the very last breath,
The moment your soul could fly.

You left me like a feather, like a butterfly,
Soft and peaceful.
Another gift of love I will treasure forever. ✷

Eau de Mom

LINDA DONAHUE

Old walnut writing desk,
dainty, designed for a petit lady,
lovingly polished with lemon Pledge
for fifty years…my mother's desk,
a gift to me when she no longer
understood the uses of pen and paper.
All she's written in months is a cipher,
three strange non-words penciled
in a child's hand on a cloth napkin.

Daddy had his den, but Mom's cloister
was her desk in the bedroom corner.
There she composed letters,

wrote grocery lists, paid the bills,
signed and addressed Christmas cards,
jotted notes in a steno-pad journal:
furniture delivery, picked peaches,
girls home snow day…just a record
of events, never anything introspective.
She worked her crosswords and played
solitaire on the sloping surface of her desk.
The cards slid downhill onto the floor.

Mom's desk is in our living room now,
another piece of her past discarded
along the road to the promised land,
Alzheimer's promised land of no return.
Her presence emanates from the desk like scent.
I can't sit there now.
I look longingly at Mom's desk but can't sit there.
I'd be saying her life is over if I sat in her place.
I'm not ready to say it. ✢

Decoration

LINDA NAGATA

Small round gold frame
Surfaces in the Christmas decorations
Tiny cross-stitches of red form a G
Intertwined cross-stitches of green form
SMACK, I'm hit again with memories. ✢

There is one remaining drawer.
A Pandora's box. A flood of anxiety
increases my heartbeats. I don't want any secrets, no remnants of
any grief or pain of her life. She had enough with Alzheimer's.

Let this be a simple walk
through old paid bills and
receipts.

FRANCES KAKUGAWA

I slowly pull out the drawer. It is
packed with cards and envelopes.
Oh no! Outdated checks? A birth certificate of my illegitimate birth?
No, they are Mother's Day cards, many browned with age,
collected throughout the years.
Many don't even hold a handwritten message of love.
They were all Hallmarks and she had kept them all.

Beneath the cards, a handkerchief. A square piece of now
yellowed handkerchief edged with bright green lace.
Memory sinks in; I had made that fifty-six years ago,
for Mother's Day.

Once a week, we spent an hour called Practical Arts
with the cafeteria manager at Kapoho School.
It was probably a way to give teachers, all three of them
in Grades One to Six, an hour off. Girls learned to crochet doilies,
while the boys grabbed hoes and weeders.
I was in the fifth grade: I had painstakingly crocheted a delicate row of
bright green lace around the edge of a square piece of

white muslin cloth.
I don't think my mother ever used it.

My mother liked to save things for a better day. In her closets,
robes, sweaters and nightgowns, with their tags hanging like
upside down bats.
"I'll save this when I go to the hospital." She never did
go to the hospital until she had a minor stroke before her diagnosis.

This handkerchief was probably "too good to be used,"
saved for a tea date with the queen someday. Or maybe
an evening out with Lawrence Welk. Oh, how she loved
Lawerence Welk. She worried when he danced his jig a bit too fast.
"You'll get heart attack!" she warned him at the screen. He was
her weekly Saturday night date. I wished then, I could have
tossed some magical stars to send her on the floor
with Mr. Welk, dancing to his one-ah-two-ah-three.

I toss out the old Mother's Day cards, but save the handkerchief.
I use it as a doily now and each time I see it, I smile, remembering,
adding my own fantasy: Each time she had opened her drawer,
she was on the dance floor with Lawrence Welk, waltzing away
with the handkerchief held gently against his back.
And for a moment, she was given a life of glamour
in her quiet life in Kapoho. ❧

and yet, and yet...

now there are Sunday mornings
of crossword puzzles
filled in one sitting...
invitations RSVP-ed in ink,
spur-of-the moment outings
to theaters and malls...
conversations with adults:
an art once lost, best-selling novels
beginning to end...
no late fees
on credit card bills,
or unsent Christmas cards in May...
time and self again,
in the river that keeps flowing
in loss and relief.

Is there life after caregiving? Yes, and just as we slowly evolved into caregiving, life after caregiving demands a similar, slow process of redesigning a new life.

If, during caregiving, we believe that our lives are on hold, that

Life After Caregiving
· CHAPTER TWELVE ·

leaves a constant yearning—to return to a place we can no longer return—and this barricades us from being fully in the present. My life was not on hold, my life was simply redesigned to take another form, that of a caregiver, and I embraced this new life, living in the present, doing the best I could. Genie Mitchell, in her poem "What I Know" (page 249) says it best. Ironically, after caregiving was over, I had changed and couldn't return to the life I had before caregiving. For example, I couldn't return to my golf game and flute lessons. Life took on a different path. In Jason Kimura's case, his role as son to his father began to transform soon after the death of his mother; he, too, could not simply pick up the life he had before.

Soon after my mother's death, I tried to fill the space she had left with activities. One day I began exploring this space I was trying so hard to refill. In exploring that space through poetry, I came to an enlightened discovery: It's all right to grieve. It's all right to preserve and live with that empty space, for it brings in a flowing river, streaming without obstruction. Go to that space, dwell in it until that space is slowly melded into your own life space as a single whole.

After caregiving is done, there is the clarity of hindsight. *I wish I had… I should have… I wish I could go back…* There is so much wisdom in hindsight, wisdom that can't be taken back in time to when we were caregivers. Being stuck on all the "should have"s can only nurture guilt and remorse, a rather useless occupation. Why don't we take this hindsight and use it to help others—as we said in that childhood game, "Pass on, no pass back." There is no perfection and we did the best we could.

Why do you say I am sacrificing
good years of my life
for caring for my mother,
when it shouldn't be a secret

What I Know

EUGENIE MITCHELL

that I am really living
in a way I have never lived
before?

I know I am holed-up here,
rarely venturing out,
floundering under mountains of Mom's possessions,
warehousing my profession,
eradicating my retirement,
undermining my health,
foregoing friendships, travel, restaurants, books and movies,
growing fatter, greyer, paler and more wrinkled,
all while doing daily drudgery.

No, this is not sacrifice.
It is just reality.
I am really living
in a way I have never lived before.
I am living love.

The gift of the last New Moon, April, 2005.

Seven years of caregiving for my father.

A night of meaningful dreams,

Showing me

The Most Important Thing

JODY MISHAN

That I need to be a better mother to myself.

Realizing that if a nuclear bomb

Were to go off and destroy the world tomorrow,

I would still spend my last day

Caring for Dad as best I could,

Because he can do nothing for himself anymore.

Because now is the time that he needs me the most.

Later on when he has passed,

And I am older,

I will miss him,

And wish for just one more hour or day in his presence.

I'll remember that I was there for him

At the crucial time,

The important time.

I smiled in my sleep all night,

Waking from dreams,

Repeating this one rarely felt and precious certainty,

"This is the most important thing I could be doing right now."

It brought me great joy and peace

Which will sustain me until it is his time to go.

Where do epiphanies like this come from?

Small moments within light years of routine,
Sadness, anger, despair, boredom.
The New Moon in April brought it,
Grace to heal my soul for awhile,
Light in the darkness, night-blooming flower. ✑

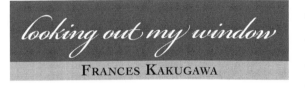

FRANCES KAKUGAWA

three robins pecking in
unison
on freshly mowed lawn,
it must be spring.

crepe myrtle displaying naked limbs
wrapped in emeralds and jades.
rosemary shooting blossoms
in lavender and pinks,
green turtle basking on a rock
in a fishpond.
yes, it must be spring
my feet, still frozen in last winter's slush,
paralyzed. is it truly spring? ✑

December 11, 2001

My father stood on the edge of the concrete walkway, the sun brittle on his frowning face, defining the sharp lines of age and

worry. We had just concluded a meeting with his accountant to discuss inheritance and estate taxes because of Mom's death.

So now we stood outside the accountant's office, about to part company, to retrieve our respective cars, to drive off to our connected but separate lives.

I could tell he did not grasp the ledger-lined logic and tax coded conversation from which we had just escaped. I didn't blame him. I barely understood it myself, numbers not being my strength.

"Don't worry about it," I said, indicating with my tone that I would take care of it, but my shoulders sank, just a little bit, at the thought of it. I remember a time not so long ago when it was he who hid worries behind a smooth brow, and assured *me* that he would take care of all. A mere twenty-five years had not only taken my mother's life, but had sucked out most of my father's as well. Now I have taken his place as guardian, only to be one day replaced. How quickly I have fallen into the groove of this inescapable cycle, when I had thought I was somehow immune.

The maker's gone...
Her web dangles
In the wind,
As each thread

Strangles with dust.

The Web

FRANCES KAKUGAWA

This silken web
Once splendored many,

But that was when
There was a womb.

When I am gone,
Will you say
I was here? ✻

Why are we taught since childhood days
To always fill in the spaces?
Before our fingers are able to curl
Around a crayon,

Empty Spaces
FRANCES KAKUGAWA

We are given coloring books
To fill in the spaces.
From early childhood we are
taught,

Not to stray beyond the lines…
To always fill in the spaces.
All of my life I have lived
With crayons in one hand,
Filling in spaces,
Spaces left by departed lovers, family, friends,
Leaving me crayons smashed against walls
Creating more grief than art.
Today, another space created by her flight.
But this space I will not fill
With any color, stroke or art.
This space bears her name.
To this place I will return time and again,
To be immersed in love, grief, sadness, memories.
This place where all feelings dwell…
No longer a battlefield
Between crayons and me.
This place I will honor and love
For as long as it holds her name. ✄

It is that time,
Whether clocked at Pacific, Eastern
Or Greenwich Mean,
For that relentless ache
To slowly overtake Sunday afternoons,

Sundays at 5 P.M.

FRANCES KAKUGAWA

An ache that has no name,
Just an ache of emptiness,
Unfulfilled dreams and
Unlived moments yet to come.

It is also that time for healing…

A time to smooth jagged edges
Of shattered crystals crunching
Under naked feet.
A time to tweeze each splinter of pain
From broken skin
Of the young and the aged.
It is a time for forgiving…
A time to unlatch doors
Of the caged,
So each can soar to its destination
With messages of peace.

It is a time for solitude,
La Boheme, the blues.
It is, above everything else,
A hell of a time
For being a woman
Who was not born
For Sunday afternoons. ❧

My house was once so cluttered,
I had no room to move.
No space to step about,
No place to call sweet home.

Clutter

FRANCES KAKUGAWA

The garbage, waste and residue
Soon stacked against my door,
Locking me in, frozen and chained
Within my own prison walls.

To live or die, to be jailed or free,
Only I could find that key.

My house is now less cluttered,
I've done a lot of cleaning,
Guilt, regrets, falsehoods and despair
No longer fill every space.

Windows are glistening,
Sunlight's peeking through,
Beyond the door, the world awaits
For my return. ✤

Last night, my mother died again.
This time, the tears
Eroded and washed down walls
Until there was nothing left,

A Dream

FRANCES KAKUGAWA

But remnants of my grief.

There were no tears
The first time she died.
I pulled in the reins,

As I did, all those years,
Caring for her.
I never let go, so afraid
I'd run away
And never be caught.

When she died,
All those years of reining in
Froze the rivers
That wanted free.

She died again last night.
I cried and screamed
All the grief I held.
I tore off the reins
From my flesh
And let the tears
Wash and cleanse
Until morning nudged me
To a new day. ✤

We suspected it might be, but maybe not.
Maybe papal dispensation, miracle medication,
temporary reprieve, even simple serendipity...
something, *anything*, would intervene to delay

the inevitable: our last Christmas with Mom.

What if our suspicions proved true and
this was it,

the last Christmas we'd spend together as a family?
We knew it had to happen, and soon: this year,
next year, soon...We would be ready just in case.
We would make this Christmas memorable.

We waited for Mom in the entrance hall,
anticipating her smile, unprepared for what
followed: we were strangers, and she was
afraid of us. She backed away and clung
to an aide, fear all over her face.

Deflated as a punctured plastic Santa,
we left without her. The numbing truth
that our last Christmas with Mom had
already taken place, that this would be our
first without her, suddenly penetrated.

If only we'd known last year,
we would have polished the silver,
washed the crystal, ironed the napkins,

served her ham and scalloped potatoes
instead of that new fusion cuisine
from *Gourmet Magazine*, made the house
sparkle with lights and tinsel and strings
of beads on an old-fashioned tree, played
carols and Nat King Cole on the stereo
instead of *Twisted Christmas*…

If only there were a way to know last
times before they happen. Or would
prescience be too heavy a burden, heavier
than today's heartache and regret that
hindsight is all we get? ❧

My mother was never demonstrative.
I don't think she ever said she loved me.

Words of Love From the Memory Care Ward

LINDA DONAHUE

Yet she was the
vital pulse in my
veins,
    doing what
she did on the
periphery of my vision
    so quietly and steadily that I rarely noticed.
Her domain was the routine, the mundane,

the boring, repetitive stuff.
She did what had to be done without complaint.

My eccentric, domineering dad eclipsed my mom
      until she became almost invisible.
Even today I don't know everything she did for me,
      unseen and unacknowledged.
What I do remember is her patient, unobtrusive presence,
      offstage but always there.
I took so much for granted:
      ironed tablecloths and matching china,
      clean folded laundry smelling of sunshine,
      banana bread and buttermilk cookies baking,
      applesauce simmering on the stove, never store-bought,
      home-sewn Halloween costumes,
      vases filled with iris and peonies,
all murmuring the words of love her mouth couldn't form
      and I couldn't hear.

Now Mom tells me every day that she loves me,
      that she couldn't manage without me,
      that I'm a good girl.
I've waited a lifetime to hear those words.
I could have heard them so much sooner had I listened.
I hear you now, Mom. I hear you. ☙

I am a poem
And I am ageless.

When I was one and twenty

The Autumn Moon Hangs

FRANCES KAKUGAWA

I spoke of lingering sunsets into night,

Envying that solitary bird flapping vigorously,
Racing the sinking sun at end of day.

Decades and one later
I am still poem.
I am that sunset, sinking into the sea.
That golden leaf, waiting for that last fatal breeze.
I am that Autumn moon hanging
Over crayoned fields, now free of summer harvest,
Waiting for the last flight home.

I am still poem.
I am ageless. ✻

To the caregivers and their loved ones whose names and work appear in this book: Thank you for allowing me to use your work in the hope of helping others. Your willingness to take us into your private world to help preserve the true essence of what it means to be a caregiver is indeed a gift to all.

Acknowledgments

To the Alzheimer's Association chapters in Honolulu, Hawai'i, and Sacramento, California: Thank you for your continuous interest and work by sponsoring our writing support groups throughout these years.

To Watermark Publishing's Duane Kurisu and George Engebretson: Your continued interest in reaching out to the caregiving community through my work has been most gratifying and effective.

To Watermark Publishing's Dawn Sakamoto, Director of Sales and Marketing: Thank you for all the work that you do on my behalf. I picture you sitting at your computer just waiting for my emails because your responses to my SOS for help are always immediate. Your patience and professional expertise are deeply appreciated.

To *The Hawai'i Herald*'s Karleen Chinen and staff: How do I thank you for giving me a platform to reach the community through my "Dear Frances" advice column for caregivers in your publication? It's a privilege and honor to work with you in the hope of making a difference in the lives of others.

To entertainment writer Wayne Harada: My name has appeared in your column throughout these years. It's my turn now to print your name. Thank you for keeping my work alive in the Islands through your "Show Biz" column.

To Michelle Johnston, Regional Director of the Alzheimer's Association, Northern California & Northern Nevada Chapter and Mike Splaine, Policy Adviser, Alzheimer's Disease International: Thank you for your words of praise for this book and your support for my work in the past. Your approbation means a great deal to me, personally and professionally.

Last and not least, a word of gratitude to all the organizations throughout the United States for your invitations to share my work with caregivers and health care professionals. And to the thousands of caregivers I have met, thank you for inspiring me to continue working with caregivers and their loved ones.

Author, educator and inspirational speaker Frances H. Kakugawa is an advocate of the power of writing to enrich our lives. As a caregiver for her late mother, Matsue, who was afflicted with Alzheimer's disease, Frances found that poetry and journaling helped her bring dignity and compassion to the caregiving experience. As a result, she started poetry and journaling support groups for other caregivers in Hawai'i and in Sacramento, California. Through her writings, workshops, school visits, readings and speaking engagements nationwide she helps others embrace caregiving and, through their writing, discover their own humanity.

Frances was born and raised on the Big Island of Hawai'i in Kapoho, a plantation village covered by lava flows. During her years as an educator, she taught in Hawai'i, Micronesia and Michigan and lectured at the University of Hawai'i. She is the recipient of the Hawai'i-Pacific Gerontological Society Award for her work with the elderly and appears in *Living Legacy: Outstanding Japanese Women of the 20th Century in Hawai'i*.

Among her eleven books are three on Alzheimer's and caregiving: *Mosaic Moon: Caregiving Through Poetry* (Watermark Publishing, 2002); a children's book, *Wordsworth Dances the Waltz* (Watermark Publishing, 2007) and *Breaking the Silence: A Caregiver's Voice* (Willow Valley Press, 2010).

In addition to running her workshops and giving lectures, Frances writes a monthly advice column for caregivers, "Dear Frances," in *The Hawai'i Herald*. She also blogs regularly about caregiving, writing and life on her blog at franceskakugawa. wordpress.org. She presently resides in Sacramento, California.

18137298R00150

Made in the USA
San Bernardino, CA
31 December 2014